THOMAS HARDY'S CHRISTMAS

The frontispiece for the 1878 illustrated edition of Under the Greenwood Tree, *by R. Knights.*

THOMAS HARDY'S CHRISTMAS

Compiled by

JOHN CHANDLER

SUTTON PUBLISHING

First published in the United Kingdom in 1997
Sutton Publishing Limited · Phoenix Mill · Thrupp
Stroud · Gloucestershire · GL5 2BU

British Library Cataloguing in Publication Data
A catalogue record for this book is available from the British Library

ISBN 0-7509-1434-3

Dedicated to Desmond Hawkins

 TM   ALAN SUTTON™ and SUTTON™ are the
trade marks of Sutton Publishing Limited

Typeset in 11/15pt Sabon.
Typesetting and origination by
Sutton Publishing Limited
Printed in Great Britain by
Ebenezer Baylis, Worcester.

CONTENTS

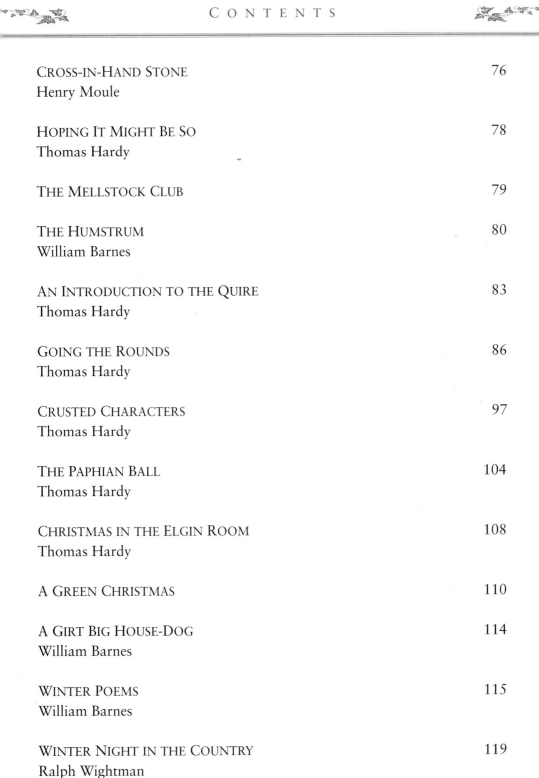

A Momentary Illumination

Llewelyn Powys

Christmas Eve, 1911, and two brothers set off for a wet walk home after shopping in Dorchester. Their route takes them past Max Gate, the house which Thomas Hardy had built a quarter of a century earlier as his home, and where he was to spend more than forty Christmases. It would be here too, on Christmas Day 1927, that he would put pencil to paper for the last time.

It was growing dark before we were ready to leave the gay, lighted streets, which, in spite of the heavy downpour, were so filled with festive faces. Theodore had bought a sledge-hammer for breaking up his coal, and with this primitive implement over his shoulder we began our walk, the rain blowing in gusts against our muffled figures, the naked hedgerows on each side of the old Wareham highway only dimly visible. A glimmer of light shone through the trees surrounding Max Gate. We thought of the old man, in there, sitting by his apple-wood fire, brooding on God knows how many past Christmas nights; the old man whom we so loved and honoured, wise as the oldest owl in Yellham Woods. On we went, the sentinel elms by the field-gates appearing and disappearing. Now and then, a tranter's van would overtake us, its dim, swaying lantern throwing upon our drenched forms a momentary illumination.

A winter night's impression of Max Gate, by Donald Maxwell, first published in his Unknown Dorset *in 1927.*

Yuletide in a Younger World

Thomas Hardy

Retrospection, indeed, filled Hardy's last years, and in many of his later poems he wistfully reflected on the rose-tinted memories of youthful celebration. For him, as for most of us, the arrival of Christmas and the passing of the year increased the pangs of his nostalgia, and teased from him some of his finest and most characteristic poetry.

Illustration by Albert Rutherston to accompany Ariel Poems edition of Yuletide in a Younger World, *1927.*

We believed in highdays then,
And could glimpse at night
On Christmas Eve
Imminent oncomings of radiant revel—
Doings of delight: —
Now we have no such sight.

We had eyes for phantoms then,
And at bridge or stile
On Christmas Eve
Clear beheld those countless ones who had crossed it
Cross again in file: —
Such has ceased longwhile!

We liked divination then,
And, as they homeward wound
On Christmas Eve,
We could read men's dreams within them spinning
Even as wheels spin round: —
Now we are blinker-bound.

We heard still small voices then,
And, in the dim serene
Of Christmas Eve,
Caught the fartime tones of fire-filled prophets
Long on earth unseen . . .
— Can such ever have been?

The House of Hospitalities

Thomas Hardy

Thomas Hardy was born in 1840 at Higher Bockhampton, a hamlet of smallholdings and cottages close to Dorchester, the county town of Dorset. His father earned his living as a builder, and was an amateur musician in his spare time, playing the violin for local dances and in the nearby parish church at Stinsford. His mother, the more dominant partner, was a natural storyteller and a voracious reader.

Hardy's childhood, defined by the activities and beliefs of his parents, relatives, and neighbours within the hamlet of Higher Bockhampton, set him up with that garner of rural custom and folklore upon which he was to draw so memorably throughout his writing career. From his father (and grandfather before him) he inherited an enthusiasm for music and dancing, and these were given full rein at the round of parties each Christmas.

In 1924 a visit to an old barn, one of the venues for his youthful music-making, left him wishing that he had not tried to revive a scene from a distant past, seventy years before. But this poem, published in 1909 and recalling Christmas parties in a neighbour's house, betrayed as yet no such regrets.

Here we broached the Christmas barrel,
Pushed up the charred log-ends;
Here we sang the Christmas carol,
And called in friends.

Time has tired me since we met here
When the folk now dead were young,
Since the viands were outset here
And quaint songs sung.

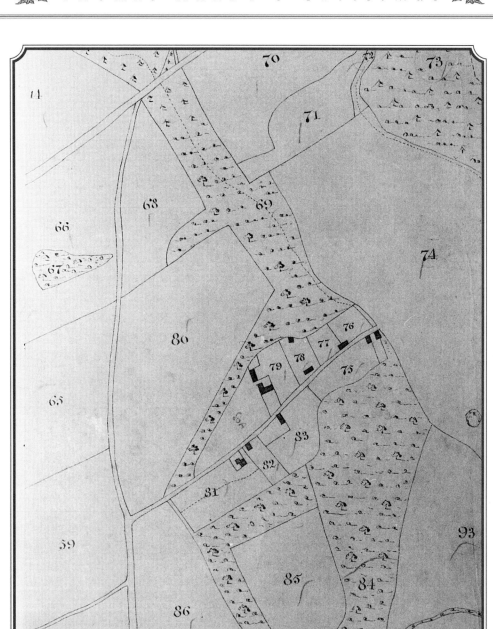

Part of Stinsford Tithe Map, showing Higher Bockhampton in 1839, the year of Hardy's conception. Hardy's father and grandmother lived in the cottage numbered 75, and his uncle lived opposite at 77. William Keats, a tranter, lived at 76, and his brother Charles at 83; they, and Hardy's father, are the models for the Dewy family, prominent members of the Mellstock Quire.

And the worm has bored the viol
That used to lead the tune,
Rust has eaten out the dial
That struck night's noon.

Now no Christmas brings in neighbours,
And the New Year comes unlit;
Where we sang the mole now labours,
And spiders knit.

Yet at midnight if here walking,
When the moon sheets wall and tree,
I see forms of old time talking,
Who smile on me.

The Tranter's Party

Thomas Hardy

*Dancing, among the community of Hardy's childhood, was
not allowed on Christmas Day itself, since, as Mrs Penny
declared:*

'If you do have a party on Christmas-night, 'tis only fair and honourable
to the sky-folk to have it a sit-still party. Jigging parties be all very well
on the Devil's holidays; but a jigging party looks suspicious now. O yes; stop
till the clock strikes, young folk – so say I.'

It happened that some warm mead accidentally got into Mr Spink's head
about this time.

'Dancing,' he said, 'is a most strengthening, livening, and courting
movement, 'specially with a little beverage added! And dancing is good . . .'

But wait they must, until the dial had 'struck night's noon'. Then the tranter's party, described in Under the Greenwood Tree, *could begin in earnest. First the instruments were tuned; then the company jockeyed for position; coquettishness, ardour, and timidity were all apparent as the dance proceeded. The pace quickened.*

The ear-rings of the ladies now flung themselves wildly about, turning violent summersaults, banging this way and that, and then swinging quietly against the ears sustaining them. Mrs Crumpler – a heavy woman, who, for some reason which nobody ever thought worth inquiry, danced in a clean apron – moved so smoothly through the figure that her feet were never seen, conveying to imaginative minds the idea that she rolled on castors.

Minute after minute glided by, and the party reached the period when ladies' back-hair begins to look forgotten and dissipated; when a perceptible dampness makes itself apparent upon the faces even of delicate girls – a ghastly dew having for some time rained from the features of their masculine partners; when skirts begin to be torn out of their gathers; when elderly people, who have stood up to please their juniors, begin to feel sundry small tremblings in the region of their knees, and to wish the interminable dance was at Jericho; when (at country parties of the thorough sort) waistcoats begin to be unbuttoned, and when the fiddlers' chairs have been wriggled, by the frantic bowing of their occupiers, to a distance of about two feet from where they originally stood.

THE TRANTER.

'The Tranter', by R. Knights, for the 1878 illustrated edition of Under the Greenwood Tree.

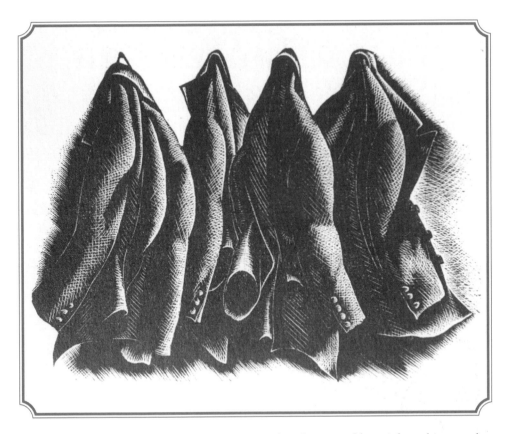

'"Before we begin," said the Tranter, "my proposal is, that 'twoud be a right and proper plan for every mortal man in the dance to pull off his jacket, considering the heat."' Wood engraving by Clare Leighton for the 1940 illustrated edition of Under the Greenwood Tree.

Hardy's earliest portrayal of Christmas among his Dorset neighbours supplied the opening to his first novel, The Poor Man and the Lady, *which he wrote in 1868 when he was twenty-eight and working as an architect's assistant. It was never published, and the manuscript has not survived. But from it he appears to have rescued the Christmas episode and adapted it for* Under the Greenwood Tree, *so that it has become one of the best-loved evocations of country merry-making in English literature. We shall sample more of it later.*

Herrenston

William Barnes

Although the best-known, the festivities at Hardy's Mellstock were by no means the only Christmas celebrations in the Victorian countryside around Dorchester to have been recorded in print. An hour's walk from Stinsford (alias Mellstock) stands a group of three villages, all with the prefix Winterbourne – Herringston, Monkton and Came. It was at the ancient manor house of Herringston that Christmas celebrations were recalled in dialect verse by a poet whom Hardy greatly admired, William Barnes.

Zoo then the leady an' the squier,
At Chris'mas, gatherd girt an' small,
Vor me'th, avore their roaren vier,
An' roun' their bwoard, 'ithin the hall;
An' there, in glitt'ren rows, between
The roun'-rimm'd pleates, our knives did sheen,
Wi' frothy eale, an' cup an' can,
Vor maid an' man, at Herrenston.

An' there the jeints o' beef did stand,
Lik' cliffs o' rock, in goodly row;
Where woone mid quarry till his hand
Did tire, an' meake but little show;
An' after we'd a-took our seat,
An' greace had been a-zaid vor meat,
We zet to work, an' zoo begun
Our feast an' fun at Herrenston.

An' mothers there, bezide the bwoards,
Wi' little childern in their laps,
Did stoop, wi' loven looks an' words,
An' veed em up wi' bits an' draps;

An' smilen husbands went in quest
O' what their wives did like the best;
An' you'd ha' zeed a happy zight,
Thik merry night, at Herrenston.

An' then the band, wi' each his leaf
O' notes, above us at the zide,
Play'd up the praise ov England's beef
An' vill'd our hearts wi' English pride;
An' leafy chains o' garlands hung,
Wi' dazzlen stripes o' flags, that swung
Above us, in a bleaze o' light,
Thik happy night, at Herrenston.

An' then the clerk, avore the vier,
Begun to lead, wi' smilen feace,
A carol, wi' the Monkton quire,
That rung drough all the crowded pleace.
An' dins o' words an' laughter broke
In merry peals drough clouds o' smoke;
Vor hardly wer there woone that spoke,
But pass'd a joke, at Herrenston.

Then man an' maid stood up by twos,
In rows, drough passage, out to door,
An' gaily beat, wi' nimble shoes,
A dance upon the stwonen vloor.
But who is worthy vor to tell,
If she that then did bear the bell,
Wer woone o' Monkton, or o' Ceame,
Or zome sweet neame ov Herrenston.

Zoo peace betide the girt vo'k's land,
When they can stoop, wi' kindly smile,
An' teake a poor man by the hand,
An' cheer en in his daily tweil.

An' oh! mid He that's vur above
The highest here, reward their love,
An' gi'e their happy souls, drough greace,
A higher pleace than Herrenston.

Mary Frampton's Journal

It may have been open house at Herringston, but at Moreton, a few miles further down the Frome valley, the squire and his family seem one year to have kept their celebrations and interesting traditions to themselves. This was perhaps understandable since it was the uneasy Christmas of 1830, when a few weeks previously many Dorset labourers had been in open revolt for higher wages, and were now awaiting their fate in gaol.

Our Christmas was passed with a large family party at Moreton. The house was unbarred and unblockaded with the exception of the one large window on the staircase. The carol singers from Mr Frampton's own parishes ushered in Christmas Eve and Christmas Morn as usual, but no mummers were allowed to perform their ancient drama of the wonderful recovery of a man killed in battle by a little bottle of elixir drawn from the pocket of the doctor of the piece, or to personify the 'Senses' from the ancient mysteries with their Latin names, Tactus, Visus, etc. The yule log, however, burnt on the large hearth of the entrance hall. The peacock in full plummage with its fiery mouth was placed on the dinner table, with of course the boar's head; the immense candles were well covered with laurel. The hare appeared with the red herring astride on its back, and the wassail bowl and lamb's wool were not inferior to former years.

Alice Smith's Birthday

Between Stinsford and the great house at Moreton lay the village of West Stafford. Its rectory was occupied by the Smith family, inveterate diarists, and in later years friends of the Hardys. Thomas Hardy once went to stay with Bosworth Smith (Boz or Bos in the diaries) at Harrow, where he was a housemaster, and Evangeline (Eva) became the author of three published novels.

It is always a pleasure to find that Victorian diaries have survived. Here, most unusually, we have two diaries describing the same event, Christmas 1866 at West Stafford Rectory. First is mother's diary entry:

Our darling Alice's 18th Birthday [on Christmas Day]. We gave her as the joint gift of Parents and brothers and sisters a 50s. gold chain for her watch – and I added a Book of the Communion – May God give her His blessed Spirit and root and ground her in the truth and make her a true disciple of the Saviour. We heard from darling Boz himself who spoke of Mrs Jardine's refusing to let him travel yesterday for fear of consequences – and that he felt so sad to be absent for the first time on Christmas Day. Flora wrote also so nicely and sensibly, and both hope to come tomorrow. God grant he may run no risk, and be strengthened to come with real benefit! I played the Harmonium twice and had 3 Hymns at each service. We had a nice address [by] Jn Reggy before the Lord's Supper. Henry, Walter, and Alice rec'd it with me, and Jack helped Papa – Reggy preached on the Saviour's Birthday in the afternoon, 2d Luke – I sat with G' Floyer. We had the usual Xtmas Dinner at 6 – and 'Buz' after. I felt very tired and had a doze and after Tea sang.

And here is what Alice chose to record:

. . . Various bands of singers passed by house in evening [Christmas Eve]. Began W. Irving's Christmas story after Wicked Robber [a game referred to earlier]. The hall nicely decorated. In morning [Christmas Day] Mamie gave me a card case of mother-of-pearl. Heard from Mary M. Miss Bucanon sent photo of herself. Georgie Thomas and Miss Bushnan wrote and sent me an ivory bracelet. All the rest gave me a gold watch chain, and Mama a book for Communion. We gave Reggy [presumably their curate] a Xmas stocking, and stood round dining room table while he pulled the things out. Brats gave presents to the babies. I, Jag and Toby then went round to give our presents to

Wood engraving by Clare Leighton for the 1940 illustrated edition of Under the Greenwood Tree.

servants. I gave collars and cuffs. Church nicely decorated. Papa made a short sermon, stayed to sacrament, Then lunched off soup, etc. Played with Eva in the garden before 2nd church. Rather gloomy day. Bos rather better. Rainy after church. Sat with Josey and Baby. Had Xmas dinner at 6, turkey, flaming plum pudding, snapdragon, champagne, etc, etc. Reggy came down to half of it. Played Buz and Personal game after. Mama not very well. Bos wrote and seemed anxious about himself. Mrs Floyer came and saw the children.

Christmas Invitation

William Barnes

The regret when someone has to miss the celebrations (Bosworth, Alice's brother, was too ill to travel home) is also the theme of a pair of poems by William Barnes. Unlike many rhymers in dialect, Barnes was a fine poet, and any difficulties in grasping his meaning are amply repaid by the quality of his images. Hardy held his work in such esteem that in 1908, immediately after he had completed The Dynasts, *the poet turned editor and published a selection of Barnes's best poems (in which he included 'Chris'mas Invitation'). Here a whole catalogue of Christmas amusements and customs is presented for us to chew over and join in.*

Chris'mas Invitation

Come down to-morrow night; an' mind,
Don't leave thy fiddle-bag behind;
We'll sheake a lag, an' drink a cup
O' eale, to keep wold Chris'mas up.

An' let thy sister teake thy earm,
The walk won't do her any harm;
There's noo dirt now to spweil her frock,
The ground's a-vroze so hard's a rock.

William Barnes (1801–86), the Dorset poet. His life-size statue, erected in 1889, stands outside St Peter's Church in the centre of Dorchester.

You won't meet any stranger's feace,
But only naighbours o' the pleace,
An' Stowe, an' Combe; an' two or dree
Vrom uncle's up at Rookery.

An' thou wu'lt vind a rwosy feace,
An' peair ov eyes so black as sloos,
The prettiest woones in all the pleace, –
I'm sure I needen tell thee whose.

We got a back-bran', dree girt logs
So much as dree ov us can car;
We'll put em up athirt the dogs,
An' meake a vier to the bar.

An' ev'ry woone shall tell his teale,
An' ev'ry woone shall zing his zong,
An' ev'ry woone wull drink his eale
To love an' frien'ship all night long.

We'll snap the tongs, we'll have a ball,
We'll sheake the house, we'll lift the ruf,
We'll romp an' meake the maidens squall,
A-catchen o'm at blind-man's buff.

Zoo come to-morrow night; an' mind,
Don't leave thy fiddle-bag behind;
We'll sheake a lag, an' drink a cup
O' eale, to keep wold Chris'mas up.

Keepen up o' Chris'mas

An' zoo you didden come athirt,
To have zome fun last night: how wer't?
Vor we'd a-workd wi' all our might
To scour the iron things up bright,
An' brush'd an' scrubb'd the house all drough;

17

An' brought in vor a brand, a plock
O' wood so big's an uppen-stock,
An' hung a bough o' misseltoo,
An' ax'd a merry friend or two,
To keepen up o' Chris'mas.

An' there wer wold an' young; an' Bill,
Soon after dark, stalk'd up vrom mill.
An' when he wer a-comen near,
He whissled loud vor me to hear;
Then roun' my head my frock I roll'd,
An' stood in orcha'd like a post,
To meake en think I wer a ghost.
But he wer up to't, an' did scwold
To vind me stannen in the cwold,
A-keepen up o' Chris'mas.

We play'd at forfeits, an' we spun
The trencher roun', an' meade such fun!
An' had a geame o' dree-ceard loo,
An' then begun to hunt the shoe.
An' all the wold vo'k zitten near,
A-chatten roun' the vier pleace,
Did smile in woone another's feace,
An' sheake right hands wi' hearty cheer,
An' let their left hands spill their beer,
A-keepen up o' Chris'mas.

Louisa Colfox's Toast

A rather more contrived poem, welcoming Christmas guests and cataloguing other members of the family absent from the celebration, has been preserved on a scrap of notepaper now in the Dorset Record Office. It was composed by Louisa Colfox, the mistress of a well-to-do household at Bridport in west Dorset, for her to recite at dessert during the family Christmas dinner in 1867. Her home, Rax House, is mentioned at the end.

1

Though small the number meeting here
Each has the one to them most dear
And health to eat our Christmas cheer
And hope to greet the coming year

2

Love and a hearty welcome to you all
Welcome dear Mother, welcome Minnie Small
Welcome Tom's brother, welcome sister Anna
Welcome Miss Carter, in the kindest manner

3

Alfred of all the dear and hopeful heir
And Alice welcome hearth and home to share
Friends to our daughter from her birth
May ye all cheer each other whilst on earth

4

Now Father Christmas swift winged thought pray aid
Till we have many a kindly visit paid
First then to Sambourne, venerated Mother
A kiss to you, dear Ellen, your [*sic*] another

5

To Knapton House, Arthur and sister Blanche
Kind love to you, and each young olive branch
To Bognor next and here bowed down with years
Kind Uncle William – then good Kate appears.

6

Heigh presto! Now we cross Atlantic Ocean
Dear Uncle George! to you love and devotion!
Of wife and children health and home bereft
The peace, that passeth understanding thou hast left.

7

Now back again good Christmas! back to Plush
There sits Aunt Miller, silence now oh hush
In her best gown, and dignified white hair
The hour she sats [*sic*], in her nice easy chair.

8

In Grafton St. in London now we go
Forget Aunt Mary Anne, oh no, no, no
And then by taking just a little dodge
We'll drop in on our friends at Tulse Hill Lodge

9

And at the Davis's we would appear
And wish them happy Christmas and new year
At Mrs Battiscombe we'll take a peep
And solitary Kate we'll take a peep.

Now back to Rax good Christmas thus it ends
With health to all absent and present friends.

The Thieves Who Couldn't Stop Sneezing

Thomas Hardy

A Christmas feast, perhaps rather similar to that over which Mr and Mrs Colfox presided, was used by Hardy to make the setting for one of his short stories. It was never included in his collected works, and it seems to have been completely forgotten (possibly even by Hardy himself) during his lifetime. He wrote it in 1877 for the first issue of a children's annual, entitled Father Christmas: Our Little One's Budget. *Only two copies are known to survive, and it was not reprinted until 1942.*

Many years ago, when oak-trees now past their prime were about as large as elderly gentlemen's walking-sticks, there lived in Wessex a yeoman's son, whose name was Hubert. He was about fourteen years of age, and was as remarkable for his candour and lightness of heart as for his physical courage, of which, indeed, he was a little vain.

One cold Christmas Eve his father, having no other help at hand, sent him on an important errand to a small town several miles from home. He travelled on horseback, and was detained by the business till a late hour of the evening. At last, however, it was completed; he returned to the inn, the horse was saddled, and he started on his way. His journey homeward lay through the Vale of Blackmore, a fertile but somewhat lonely district, with heavy clay roads and crooked lanes. In those days, too, a great part of it was thickly wooded.

It must have been about nine o'clock when, riding along amid the overhanging trees upon his stout-legged cob Jerry, and singing a Christmas carol, to be in harmony with the season, Hubert fancied that he heard a noise among the boughs. This recalled to his mind that the spot he was traversing bore an evil name. Men had been waylaid there. He looked at Jerry, and wished he had been of any other colour than light grey; for on this account the docile animal's form was visible even here in the dense

shade. 'What do I care?' he said aloud, after a few minutes of reflection. 'Jerry's legs are too nimble to allow any highwayman to come near me.'

'Ha! ha! indeed,' was said in a deep voice; and the next moment a man darted from the thicket on his right hand, another man from the thicket on his left hand, and another from a tree-trunk a few yards ahead. Hubert's bridle was seized, he was pulled from his horse, and although he struck out with all his might, as a brave boy would naturally do, he was overpowered. His arms were tied behind him, his legs bound tightly together, and he was thrown into the ditch. The robbers, whose faces he could now dimly perceive to be artificially blackened, at once departed, leading off the horse.

As soon as Hubert had a little recovered himself, he found that by great exertion he was able to extricate his legs from the cord; but, in spite of every endeavour, his arms remained bound as fast as before. All, therefore, that he could do was rise to his feet and proceed on his way with his arms behind him, and trust to chance for getting them unfastened. He knew that it would be impossible to reach home on foot that night, and in such a condition; but he walked on. Owing to the confusion which this attack caused in his brain, he lost his way, and would have been inclined to lie down and rest till morning among the dead leaves had he not known the danger of sleeping without wrappers in a frost so severe. So he wandered further onwards, his arms wrung and numbed by the cord which pinioned him, and his heart aching for the loss of poor Jerry, who never had been known to kick, or bite, or show a single vicious habit. He was not a little glad when he discerned through the trees a distant light. Towards this he made his way, and presently found himself in front of a large mansion with flanking wings, gables, and towers, the battlements and chimneys showing their shapes against the stars.

All was silent; but the door stood wide open, it being from this door that the light shone which had attracted him. On entering he found himself in a vast apartment arranged as a dining-hall, and brilliantly illuminated. The walls were covered with a great deal of dark wainscoting, formed into moulded panels, carvings, closet-doors, and the usual fittings of a house of that kind. But what drew his attention most was the large table in the midst of the hall, úpon which was spread a sumptuous supper, as yet untouched. Chairs were placed around, and it appeared as if something had occurred to interrupt the meal just at the time when all were ready to begin.

Even had Hubert been so inclined, he could not have eaten in his helpless state, unless by dipping his mouth into the dishes, like a pig or cow. He wished first to obtain assistance; and was about to penetrate further into the house for that purpose when he heard hasty footsteps in the porch and the words, 'Be quick!' uttered in the deep voice which had reached him when he was dragged from the horse. There was only just time for him to dart under the table before three men entered the dining-hall. Peeping from beneath the hanging edges of the tablecloth, he perceived that their faces, too, were blackened, which at once removed any remaining doubts he may have felt that these were the same thieves.

'Now, then,' said the first – the man with the deep voice – 'let us hide ourselves. They will all be back again in a minute. That was a good trick to get them out of the house – eh?'

'Yes. You well imitated the cries of a man in distress,' said the second.

'Excellently,' said the third.

'But they will soon find out that it was a false alarm. Come, where shall we hide? It must be some place we can stay in for two or three hours, till all are in bed and asleep. Ah! I have it. Come this way! I have learnt that the further closet is not opened once in a twelvemonth; it will serve our purpose exactly.'

The speaker advanced into a corridor which led from the hall. Creeping a little farther forward, Hubert could discern that the closet stood at the end, facing the dining-hall. The thieves entered it, and closed the door. Hardly breathing, Hubert glided forward, to learn a little more of their intention, if possible; and, coming close, he could hear the robbers whispering about the different rooms where the jewels, plate, and other valuables of the house were kept, which they plainly meant to steal.

They had not been long in hiding when a gay chattering of ladies and gentlemen was audible on the terrace without. Hubert felt that it would not do to be caught prowling about the house, unless he wished to be taken for a robber himself; and he slipped softly back to the hall, out at the door, and stood in a dark corner of the porch, where he could see everything without being himself seen. In a moment or two a whole troop of personages came gliding past him into the house. There were an elderly gentleman and lady, eight or nine young ladies, as many young men, besides half-a-dozen men-servants and maids. The mansion had apparently been quite emptied of its occupants.

'Now, children and young people, we will resume our meal,' said the old gentleman. 'What the noise could have been I cannot understand. I never felt so certain in my life that there was a person being murdered outside my door.'

Then the ladies began saying how frightened they had been, and how they had expected an adventure, and how it had ended in nothing after all.

'Wait a while,' said Hubert to himself. 'You'll have adventure enough by-and-by, ladies.'

It appeared that the young men and women were married sons and daughters of the old couple, who had come that day to spend Christmas with their parents.

The door was then closed, Hubert being left outside in the porch. He thought this a proper moment for asking their assistance; and, since he was unable to knock with his hands, began boldly to kick the door.

'Hullo! What disturbance are you making here?' said a footman who opened it; and, seizing Hubert by the shoulder, he pulled him into the dining-hall. 'Here's a strange boy I have found making a noise in the porch, Sir Simon.'

Everybody turned.

'Bring him forward,' said Sir Simon, the old gentleman before mentioned. 'What were you doing there, my boy?'

'Why, his arms are tied!' said one of the ladies.

'Poor fellow!' said another.

Hubert at once began to explain that he had been waylaid on his journey home, robbed of his horse, and mercilessly left in this condition by the thieves.

'Only to think of it!' exclaimed Sir Simon.

'That's a likely story,' said one of the gentleman-guests, incredulously.

'Doubtful, hey?' asked Sir Simon.

'Perhaps he's a robber himself,' suggested a lady.

'There is a curiously wild wicked look about him, certainly, now that I examine him closely,' said the old mother.

Hubert blushed with shame; and, instead of continuing his story, and relating that robbers were concealed in the house, he doggedly held his tongue, and half resolved to let them find out their danger for themselves.

'Well, untie him,' said Sir Simon. 'Come, since it is Christmas Eve, we'll treat him well. Here, my lad; sit down in that empty seat at the bottom of the table, and make as good a meal as you can. When you have had your fill we will listen to more particulars of your story.'

*Dick and Fancy at the Tranter's Christmas party. Wood engraving by Clare Leighton for the 1940
illustrated edition of* Under the Greenwood Tree.

The feast then proceeded; and Hubert, now at liberty, was not at all sorry to join in. The more they ate and drank the merrier did the company become; the wine flowed freely, the logs flared up the chimney, the ladies laughed at the gentlemen's stories; in short, all went as noisily and as happily as a Christmas gathering in old times possibly could do.

Hubert, in spite of his hurt feelings at their doubts of his honesty, could not help being warmed both in mind and in body by the good cheer, the scene, and the example of hilarity set by his neighbours. At last he laughed as heartily at their stories and repartees as the old Baronet, Sir Simon, himself. When the meal was almost over one of the sons, who had drunk a little too much wine, after the manner of men in that century, said to Hubert, 'Well, my boy, how are you? Can you take a pinch of snuff?' He held out one of the snuff-boxes which were then becoming common among young and old throughout the country.

'Thank you,' said Hubert, accepting a pinch.

'Tell the ladies who you are, what you are made of, and what you can do,' the young man continued, slapping Hubert upon the shoulder.

'Certainly,' said our hero, drawing himself up, and thinking it best to put a bold face on the matter. 'I am a travelling magician.'

'Indeed!'

'What shall we hear next?'

'Can you call up spirits from the vasty deep, young wizard?'

'I can conjure up a tempest in a cupboard,' Hubert replied.

'Ha-ha!' said the old Baronet, pleasantly rubbing his hands. 'We must see this performance. Girls, don't go away: here's something to be seen.'

'Not dangerous, I hope?' said the old lady.

Hubert rose from the table. 'Hand me your snuff-box, please,' he said to the young man who had made free with him. 'And now,' he continued, 'without the least noise, follow me. If any of you speak it will break the spell.'

They promised obedience. He entered the corridor, and, taking off his shoes, went on tiptoe to the closet door, the guests advancing in a silent group at a little distance behind him. Hubert next placed a stool in front of the door, and, by standing upon it, was tall enough to reach to the top. He then, just as noiselessly, poured all the snuff from the box along the upper edge of the door, and, with a few short puffs of breath, blew the snuff through the chink into the interior of the closet. He held up his finger to the assembly, that they might be silent.

'Dear me, what's that?' said the old lady, after a minute or two had elapsed.
A suppressed sneeze had come from inside the closet.

Hubert held up his finger again.

'How very singular,' whispered Sir Simon. 'This is most interesting.'

Hubert took advantage of the moment to gently slide the bolt of the closet door into its place. 'More snuff,' he said, calmly.

'More snuff,' said Sir Simon. Two or three gentlemen passed their boxes, and the contents were blown in at the top of the closet. Another sneeze, not quite so well suppressed as the first, was heard: then another, which seemed to say that it would not be suppressed under any circumstances whatever. At length there arose a perfect storm of sneezes.

'Excellent, excellent for one so young!' said Sir Simon. 'I am much interested in this trick of throwing the voice – called, I believe, ventriloquism.'

'More snuff,' said Hubert.

'More snuff,' said Sir Simon. Sir Simon's man brought a large jar of the best scented Scotch.

Hubert once more charged the upper chink of the closet, and blew the snuff into the interior, as before. Again he charged, and again, emptying the whole contents of the jar. The tumult of sneezes became really extraordinary to listen to – there was no cessation. It was like wind, rain, and sea battling in a hurricane.

'I believe there are men inside, and that it is no trick at all!' exclaimed Sir Simon, the truth flashing on him.

'There are,' said Hubert. 'They are come to rob the house; and they are the same who stole my horse.'

The sneezes changed to spasmodic groans. One of the thieves, hearing Hubert's voice, cried, 'Oh! mercy! mercy! let us out of this!'

'Where's my horse?' said Hubert.

'Tied to the tree in the hollow behind Short's Gibbet. Mercy! mercy! let us out, or we shall die of suffocation!'

All the Christmas guests now perceived that this was no longer sport, but serious earnest. Guns and cudgels were procured; all the men-servants were called in, and arranged in position outside the closet. At a signal Hubert withdrew the bolt, and stood on the defensive. But the three robbers, far from attacking them, were found crouching in the corner, gasping for breath. They made no resistance; and, being pinioned, were placed in an out-house till the morning.

Hubert now gave the remainder of his story to the assembled company, and was profusely thanked for the services he had rendered. Sir Simon pressed him to stay over the night, and accept the use of the best bed-room the house afforded, which had been occupied by Queen Elizabeth and King Charles successively when on their visits to this part of the country. But Hubert declined, being anxious to find his horse Jerry, and to test the truth of the robbers' statements concerning him.

Several of the guests accompanied Hubert to the spot behind the gibbet, alluded to by the thieves as where Jerry was hidden. When they reached the knoll and looked over, behold! there the horse stood, uninjured, and quite unconcerned. At sight of Hubert he neighed joyfully; and nothing could exceed Hubert's gladness at finding him. He mounted, wished his friends 'Good-night!' and cantered off in the direction they pointed out as his nearest way, reaching home safely about four o'clock in the morning.

Playing Forfeits

John Symonds Udal

The quickening pace of life in Victorian England, the shrinking of horizons as the railways linked country to town, and the mass migration of impoverished village families to sprawling cities, all threatened to erode rural traditions, and to destroy patterns of life that had evolved over centuries. In consequence there grew among the reading public a feeling of nostalgia for the world that was embedded in nearly everyone's past, but was being forgotten. Hardy's novels caught this mood, and helped to foster it.

The customs and folklore which he described were also being studied, in a more scholarly way, by the late Victorian antiquaries. In Dorset, the leading folklorist of the period Hardy counted as a friend, John Symonds Udal. He pursued a long and eminent career as a barrister, judge, and colonial administrator, which took him to Fiji, and ultimately to the Leeward Islands, where he held the post of Chief

*Justice. In 1911 he retired and began to write up his folklore notes.
His book was eventually published in 1922, three years before his
death. It incorporated many pieces which he had written for journals
years before, including notes on 'Christmas in Dorsetshire'. Here,
following on from the supposed conjuring trick of Hardy's children's
story, are Udal's remarks about the popular Christmas game of
forfeits.*

Playing forfeits was a very favourite amusement with Dorset folk during the long winter evenings, and more particularly at Christmas-tide, when the family circle had generally more than its usual complement. There should be, if possible, twenty or thirty present to play forfeits properly, who arrange themselves round the room as conveniently as possible, and should be careful to be provided with some trifling article wherewith to pay the forfeits should any be incurred.

In some places the players sit in two lines opposite each other, each holding in his or her hand a piece of paper, or pencil, or thimble, or some such slight article, wherewith to pay their forfeit in case they should make a mistake in answering.

A common form of playing forfeits was that of a game which involved a question and answer. Two persons sat in front of the party, one of whom says as follows: 'Here's a poor old sailor just come from the sea, pray what have you got to give him?' Whoever is called upon to answer the question must be careful not to mention the word 'red', 'white,' 'blue' or 'black', or even, sometimes, give the name of any colour at all; and must not say 'yes' or 'no', in default of which she or he will have to pay a forfeit. The questioner then passes on to the next one, and says: 'Here's a poor old sailor just come from sea, pray what have you got to give him?' The one questioned must be careful only to answer, 'Nothing at all.' The other replies, 'Nothing at all!' and with an insinuating attempt to obtain an answer that will subject the speaker to a forfeit will add, 'Not a red coat?' or 'Not a blue hat?' On the person interrogated persisting in replying 'Nothing at all', the other moves on, in the hope of getting a more favourable response out of another player; and so on, until the questioner has gone all round. After this has been done, any forfeits that may have been obtained have to be redeemed by those persons who have been so unfortunate as to incur them.

Another form of playing forfeits was called 'Yes, No, Black, and White', these being the four words which must not be mentioned in the answer. In this game any kind of question was permitted.

This was sometimes called 'The old soldier', when each of the party in turn must take a poker in the right hand and knock, and, passing it to his neighbour with the left, say: 'An old soldier is come to town, what will you please to give him? You may answer whatever you like, except 'yes', 'no', 'white', or 'black'. The object is to induce the person interrogated to use one or other of these words, when a forfeit occurs.

Another form the game would sometimes take was that of a 'word puzzle', when an outlandish single word, or a curiously involved sentence had to be repeated several times (seven or nine was the usual number) without a mistake; on failure of which a forfeit was exacted.

The following is a specimen of such a word:

'Aldibirondifosdiforniosdikos.'

and this of a sentence:

'Of all the saws I ever saw saw, I never saw a saw saw as that saw saws.'

Here is another of a slightly different character in a versified form:

A twister of twist once twisted a twist,
And the twist that he twisted was a three-twisted twist;
But in twisting the twist one twist came untwisted,
And the twist that untwisted untwisted the twist.

There is another one, which I can give but imperfectly, for I can only remember up to 'twelve,' though I fancy there are 'eighteen' or more; and an old Dorsetshire lady from whom I have heard it has now (in her ninetieth year) forgotten it. It is as follows, and each rhyme is to be repeated backwards as in the last:

A gaping, wide-mouthed, waddling frog,
Two pudding-ends won't choke a dog;
Three monkeys tied to a log

Four mares stuck in a bog;
Five puppy-dogs and our dog Ball
Loudly for their breakfast call;
Six beetles on a wall,
Close to an old woman's apple-stall;
Seven lobsters in a dish,
As good as any heart can wish;
Eight cobblers, cobblers all,
Working with their tools and awl;
Nine comets in the sky,
Some are low and some are high;
Ten peacocks in the air,
I wonder how they all got there—
You don't know and I don't care;
Eleven ships sailing on the main,
Some bound for France and some for Spain,
I wish them all safe back again;
Twelve hunters, hares, and hounds,
Hunting over other men's grounds.

The redemption of the forfeits takes place in the following way. Two persons, as before, remain in front of the others, the one sitting in a chair facing the party, the other kneeling down and laying his or her head in the lap of the other, with the face downwards. The person sitting in the chair will hold the forfeited article that is about to be redeemed over the bent head of the person kneeling in front of her, and will say as follows: 'Here's a thing, and a very pretty thing! What must the owner of this pretty thing do to redeem it again?' Or, 'What must the owner do to receive it again?' Whatever the person who has his or her head in the other's lap (and who, of course, cannot see what or whose is the article held up) says what the owner of that article must do, or the forfeit cannot be redeemed, let it never be so much prized. The penalties of redemption sometimes oblige the ordeal of crawling up the chimney, or, at least, attempting to do so; or giving a sweetheart's name; or she or he may be told to 'run the gauntlet', or 'to go through purgatory', both of which have specific penalties attached to them by Dorset players; or to sing in one corner of the room, cry in another, laugh in another, and dance in another.

Sometimes the task imposed is either something which is apparently impossible to perform, such as being told 'to bite an inch off the poker', or 'to put yourself through the key-hole'; or else it is designed to make the victim ridiculous.

There are many other ways and means suggested by which the forfeits may be redeemed, and much amusement is frequently caused before the articles can be reclaimed. The game is often kept up with spirit for hours.

The Chief Amusement

John Symons Udal

No Christmas custom seemed so potent to the Victorian folklorists as the ritual drama of death and rebirth enacted by the mummers.

Chief, however, amongst the amusements and customs of this festive season – as no doubt they were the most ancient – were the 'mummers' (or maskers), a party of youths who went from house to house and performed a play or drama, generally representing a fight between St. George, the patron saint of England, and a Mohammedan leader, commemorative of the Holy Wars. The actors were all decked out with painted paper and tinsel, in the character each was intended to assume, garnished with bows, coloured strips of paper, caps, sashes, buttons, swords, helmets, etc.

The principal character in the Dorsetshire mummers was 'Old Father Christmas', who frequently appeared mounted on a wooden horse covered with trappings of dark cloth. The representation took place in the servants' hall or kitchen of the mansion or farmhouse in which the mummers were permitted (a permission seldom denied) to act. The actors, ten or twelve in number, were grouped together at the back of the stage, so to speak, and each came forward as he was required to speak or to fight, and at the conclusion fell back upon the rest, leaving the stage clear for other disputants or combatants.

As soon as the play, which always concluded with a song, was over, and the actors had been regaled with such good cheer as the hospitable hearts of the Dorsetshire folk seldom refused, the mummers passed on to the next parish, where to a fresh and ever-delighted audience they went through a repetition of their performance; and though if the night were wet and the wind cold they experienced rough usage at times, yet their welcome was made all the warmer at their next halting-place, so that none could doubt for a moment but that he came in for no small share of the delights of a 'Merry Christmas'.

Scenes of Youth

William Holloway

With their plot rooted in the Crusades, mummers' plays have long been regarded as a survival from medieval times, or even earlier. Recent work has suggested that they did not in fact become popular until the eighteenth century, and the words of most were not recorded until much later. The reminiscences in verse of a Dorset poet, William Holloway, of his childhood Christmases (he was born in 1761 near Blandford Forum) are therefore quite early evidence of mumming.

Nor yet forgotten be the festive eve,
To pageant mummeries dedicated still,
When Father Christmas to the neighbours round
His annual visit paid, in garb grotesque;
While, as he crack'd his merry jokes, and shook
His long white beard, the huddling children crept
Close to the mother's chair, and sought to hide
Beneath her apron blue each chubby face.
Prepar'd the way . . . behold a glitt'ring train;
In Sunday's best apparel, richly lac'd
Down ev'ry seam with paper, gold-emboss'd;

Of paper too aloft their ensign waves . . .
Their helmets shine with nodding plumes adorn'd,
Pluck'd from the barn-door cock, or turkey's tail;
With swords of wood, or lances, trembling white,
The peasant champions onward proudly stride,
With awkward gait, and mouth bombastic strains,
Expressive of defiance, daring loud
To single combat every bold compeer.

Foremost, St George of England . . . he who slew
The venom'd dragon . . . shakes his dreaded lance:
Th' Egyptian Soldan, and the Norman Prince . . .
The Roman Soldier, and the Turkish Knight
Come next, exulting in their proud exploits;
With others, of inferior name and note,
But not less vaunting of heroic deeds.
Out fly their swords! the clatt'ring fight begins;
While many-a little bosom anxious heaves,
To mark the dire event. Fast drop around
The vanquish'd combatants, with quiv'ring limbs;
And soon the red-brick floor is all bestrew'd
With bloodless carcases, which mimic death,
Cautious, with-eyes shut up, and breath repress'd;
While o'er the fatal field of battle stalks
The doughty victor, insolently vain,
And, wrapt in self-importance, slow retires.

Caught with the pomp and splendor of the scene,
Then would my kindled passions glow anew
With martial ardour, emulous of fame,
By judgment uncorrected . . . Such, too oft,
The Muse suspects, in nobler bosoms reign,
Prelusive to those sanguinary storms,
That waste mankind, and wrap the world in woe!

The Odd Sort of Thrill

In 1901 Thomas Hardy was interviewed for an American magazine,
The Critic, *and the conversation turned on his memories of the*
mummers.

TH: Then again, the Christmas Mummers flourished well into my
        recollection – indeed, they have not so long died out . . . Our
        mummers hereabouts gave a regular performance, 'The Play
        of St George' it was called. It contained quite a number of
        traditional characters: the Valiant Soldier, the Turkish Knight,
        St George himself, the Saracen, Father Christmas, the Fair
        Sabra, and so on. Rude as it was, the thing used to impress
        me very much – I can clearly recall the odd sort of thrill it
        would give. The performers used to carry a long staff in one
        hand and a wooden sword in the other, and pace
        monotonously round, intoning their parts on one note, and
        punctuating them by nicking the sword against the staff –
        something like this: 'Here comes I, the Valiant Soldier (nick),
        Slasher is my name (nick)'.

Interviewer: The pacing and rhythmic sing-song suggest kinship with the
        Chinese acting I have seen in San Francisco and New York.
        And what was the action of the play?

TH: I really don't know, except that it ended in a series of mortal
        combats in which all the characters but St George were killed.
        And then the curious thing was that they were invariably
        brought to life again. A personage was introduced for the
        purpose – the Doctor of Physic, wearing a cloak and a broad-
        brimmed beaver.

Interviewer: How many actors would there be in a company?

TH: Twelve to fifteen, I should think. Sometimes a large village
        would furnish forth two sets of mummers. They would go to
        the farmhouses round, between Christmas and Twelfth Night,
        doing some four or five performances each evening, and

getting ale and money at every house. Sometimes the mummers of one village would encroach on the traditional 'sphere of influence' of another village, and then there would be a battle in good earnest.

Interviewer: Did women take part in the performances?

TH: I think not – the Fair Sabra was always played by a boy. But the character was often omitted.

Interviewer: And when did the mumming go out?

TH: It went on in some neighbourhoods till 1880, or thereabouts. I have heard of a parson here and there trying to revive it; but of course that isn't at all the same thing – the spontaneity is gone.

Eustacia's Adventure

Thomas Hardy

In asking about women mummers, Hardy's interviewer showed no sign of recalling the memorable episode in The Return of the Native, *when Eustacia Vye disguised herself as a boy in order to play the part of the Turkish Knight, and join in the Egdon mummers' performance at Mrs Yeobright's Christmas party.*
Before the play of 'St George' could be performed there had to be a practice, and this took place in Captain Vye's fuel-house.

On a ledge in the fuel-house stood three tall rush-lights, and by the light of them seven or eight lads were marching about, haranguing, and confusing each other, in endeavours to perfect themselves in the play. Humphrey and Sam, the furze and turf cutters, were there looking on, so also was Timothy Fairway, who leant against the wall and prompted the boys from memory, interspersing among the set words remarks and anecdotes of the superior days when he and others were the Egdon mummers-elect that these lads were now.

Bhompston Farm near Lower Bockhampton, the original of Mrs Yeobright's house, Blooms-End, where the mummers performed in Return of the Native.

'Well, ye be as well up to it as ever ye will be,' he said. 'Not that such mumming would have passed in our time. Harry as the Saracen should strut a bit more, and John needn't holler his inside out. Beyond that perhaps you'll do . . .'

The mummers, including Eustacia in disguise, arrived at Mrs Yeobright's house at the appointed hour, to find the party in full swing. But they were stuck outside. ·

'Is there no passage inside the door, then?' asked Eustacia, as they stood within the porch.

'No,' said the lad who played the Saracen. 'The door opens right upon the front sitting-room, where the spree's going on.'

'So that we cannot open the door without stopping the dance.'

'That's it. Here we must bide till they have done, for they always bolt the back door after dark.'

'They won't be much longer,' said Father Christmas.

This assertion, however, was hardly borne out by the event. Again the instruments ended the tune; again they recommenced with as much fire and pathos as if it were the first strain. The air was now that one without any particular beginning, middle, or end, which perhaps, among all the dances which throng an inspired fiddler's fancy, best conveys the idea of the interminable – the celebrated 'Devil's Dream'. The fury of personal movement that was kindled by the fury of the notes could be approximately imagined by these outsiders under the moon, from the occasional kicks of toes and heels against the door, whenever the whirl round had been of more than customary velocity.

The first five minutes of listening was interesting enough to the mummers. The five minutes extended to ten minutes, and these to a quarter of an hour; but no signs of ceasing were audible in the lively Dream. The bumping against the door, the laughter, the stamping, were all as vigorous as ever, and the pleasure in being outside lessened considerably.

Another ten minutes passed, while the mummers debated whether or not to open the door.

At this moment the fiddles finished off with a screech, and the serpent emitted a last note that nearly lifted the roof. When, from the comparative

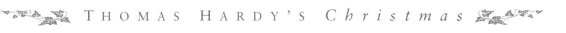

quiet within, the mummers judged that the dancers had taken their seats, Father Christmas advanced, lifted the latch, and put his head inside the door.

'Ah, the mummers, the mummers!' cried several guests at once. 'Clear a space for the mummers.'

Hump-backed Father Christmas then made a complete entry, swinging his huge club, and in a general way clearing the stage for the actors proper, while he informed the company in smart verse that he was come, welcome or welcome not; concluding his speech with:

> Make room, make room, my gallant boys,
> And give us space to rhyme;
> We've come to show Saint George's play,
> Upon this Christmas time.'

The guests were now arranging themselves at one end of the room, the fiddler was mending a string, the serpent-player was emptying his mouthpiece, and the play began. First of those outside the Valiant Soldier entered, in the interest of St George—

> 'Here come I, the Valiant Soldier;
> Slasher is my name;'

and so on. This speech concluded with a challenge to the infidel, at the end of which it was Eustacia's duty to enter as the Turkish Knight. She, with the rest who were not yet on, had hitherto remained in the moonlight which streamed under the porch. With no apparent effort or backwardness she came in, beginning—

> 'Here come I, a Turkish Knight,
> Who learnt in Turkish land to fight;
> I'll fight this man with courage bold:
> If his blood's hot I'll make it cold!'

During her declamation Eustacia held her head erect, and spoke as roughly as she could, feeling pretty secure from observation. But the concentration upon her part necessary to prevent discovery, the newness of the scene, the shine of the candles, and the confusing effect upon her vision

of the ribboned visor which hid her features, left her absolutely unable to perceive who were present as spectators. On the further side of a table bearing candles she could faintly discern faces, and that was all.

Meanwhile Jim Starks as the Valiant Soldier had come forward, and, with a glare upon the Turk, replied—

> 'If, then, thou art the Turkish Knight,
> Draw out thy sword, and let us fight!'

And fight they did; the issue of the combat being that the Valiant Soldier was slain by a preternaturally inadequate thrust from Eustacia, Jim in his ardour for genuine histrionic art, coming down like a log upon the stone floor with force enough to dislocate his shoulder. Then, after more words from the Turkish Knight, rather too faintly delivered, and statements that he'd fight St George and all his crew, St George himself magnificently entered with the well-known flourish—

> 'Here come I, Saint George, the valiant man,
> With naked sword and spear in hand,
> Who fought the dragon and brought him to the slaughter
> And by this won fair Sabra, the King of Egypt's daughter;
> What mortal man would dare to stand
> Before me with my sword in hand?'

This was the lad who had first recognised Eustacia; and when she now, as the Turk, replied with suitable defiance, and at once began the combat, the young fellow took especial care to use his sword as gently as possible. Being wounded, the Knight fell upon one knee, according to the direction. The Doctor now entered, restored the Knight by giving him a draught from the bottle which he carried, and the fight was again resumed, the Turk sinking by degrees until quite overcome – dying as hard in this venerable drama as he is said to do at the present day.

This gradual sinking to the earth was, in fact, one reason why Eustacia had thought that the part of the Turkish Knight, though not the shortest, would suit her best. A direct fall from upright to horizontal, which was the end of the other fighting characters, was not an elegant or decorous part for a girl. But it was easy to die like a Turk, by a dogged decline.

Eustacia was now among the the number of the slain, though not on the floor, for she had managed to retire into a sitting position against the clock-case, so that her head was well elevated. The play proceeded between St George, the Saracen, the Doctor, and Father Christmas; and Eustacia, having no more to do, for the first time found leisure to observe the scene around, and to search for the form that had drawn her hither . . .

The remainder of the play ended: the Saracen's head was cut off, and St George stood as victor. Nobody commented, any more than they would have commented on the fact of mushrooms coming in autumn or snowdrops in spring. They took the piece as phlegmatically as did the actors themselves. It was a phase of cheerfulness which was, as a matter of course, to be passed through every Christmas; and there was no more to be said.

They sang the plaintive chant which follows the play, during which all the dead men rise to their feet in a silent and awful manner, like the ghosts of Napoleon's soldiers in the Midnight Review.

The Mummers at Mrs Yeobright's house. Engraving, by A. Hopkins, for the serialization of
Return of the Native, *in* Belgravia, *May 1878.*

The Battle of Waterloo

In the sequence of Hardy's works The Return of the Native *is followed immediately by his novel of the Napoleonic wars,* The Trumpet Major, *which he was researching (in 1878) as the* Return *appeared in serial form. Moreover, Hardy must have been aware that many versions of the mummers' play current in his day embodied characters and actions from the Napoleonic period. Not many years later, the idea of a dramatic work based on the exploits of Nelson, Wellington and Napoleon would begin to ferment in his mind. And when, in 1904, the first part of his 'epic-drama'* The Dynasts *was published, his preface explained that he did not intend it for the stage, but for 'mental performance alone'. If his readers could not grasp such a concept, he continued:*

In respect of such plays of poesy and dream a practicable compromise may conceivably result, taking the shape of a monotonic delivery of speeches, with dreamy conventional gestures, something in the manner traditionally maintained by the old Christmas mummers, the curiously hypnotizing impressiveness of whose automatic style – that of persons who spoke by no will of their own – may be remembered by all who ever experienced it.

Some 10 miles from Hardy's home lies the village of West Lulworth and the natural harbour of Lulworth Cove. Here, in a short story dated Christmas 1882, he recounted A Tradition of 1804, *that Napoleon himself had come ashore to reconnoitre for a planned invasion. In the story the narrator, with some justification, believes that had the invasion taken place, 'we coast-folk should have been cut down one and all, and I should not have sat here to tell this tale.'*
At Lulworth a mumming play was performed on Christmas Eve every year until about 1914. It was, appropriately, a Napoleonic version, The Battle of Waterloo, *and the text has survived. It has travelled a long way from* The Play of St George; *it seems to draw elements from various sources into a confused, and at times apparently meaningless, jumble, while retaining elements of traditional mumming. A performance of the*

play was staged in Dorchester Town Hall in 1936, when a recording was made for radio.

Open your doors, and let us come in,
I hope your favour we shall win,
Whether we rise, or whether we fall,
We do our best, and endeavour to please you all.
The merry time of Christmas is now drawing near,
We hope your pockets full of money, and your cellars full of beer.
If you don't believe what I say,
Step in, old Father Christmas, and boldly clear the way.

Room, room, gallant room,
Give me room to render,
I am come to show you sports, to pass away the winter,
If you don't believe what I say,
Step in, old Father Christmas, and boldly clear the way.

Father Christmas: Here am I, old Father Christmas, welcome or welcome not,
I hope old Father Christmas will never be forgot,
Christmas comes but once a year,
And when it comes, it brings good cheer,
With a pocket full of money, and a cellar full of beer.
Now old Father Christmas have got but a short time to stay,
I means to show you sports, pleasure and pastime before I'se do go away.
I'se been out there now, I'se come back over here,
I'se like to taste a pot of thee Christmas beer,
If it be a pot of best, may your souls in Heaven to rest.
If it be a pot of small, that's better than none at all.
If you don't believe what I do say,
Step in my son, young Father Christmas, and boldly clear the way.

Young Father Christmas: Here am I, young Father Christmas, welcome or welcome not,

43

I hope young Father Christmas will never be forgot,
Although you call me young Father Christmas, my
   name is John Bull,
And I am here tonight to present you with my humble
   servant, Tom Fool.

Tom Fool: Here am I, Tom Fool. Haw, Haw, Haw. Is Mr Bull in?

John Bull: Yes, Tom, what may you want of him?

Tom Fool: I am come to tell you that Bonaparte has come
Over from France with two million of French.

John Bull: Never mind him Tom, nor all his army too,
Give me and my men the battle,
We'll show them the British Rattle.

Tom Fool: Rattle, Rattle, that will not do,
When there is rattling, there must be fighting as well as
   rattling too.
Therefore I must see what I can do.
But hark! I think I hear them coming.

Bonaparte: Here am I, Bonaparte lately come from France,
To pay John Bull a visit, and learn him a new dance,
A dance that's never been danced before, my boys, by
   any man but me.
I'll strike stirs in all your hearts, and make you Britons
   flee.

Tom Fool: Ha, Ha, but when the French do come to England, they
   will come without a heart,
Therefore tonight Mr Bull and I will try to upset proud
   Bonaparte.
Although you call me Tom Fool, there's many a man
   been made fool by me,
And by my actions here tonight, that truth you'll plainly
   see.
As for that tyrant Bonaparte, I hope for to lay down,
And with my sword in hand this night, I'll lay thee on
   the ground.

John Bull: Be silent Tom, don't interrupt that noisy fellow's breath,
Be as it will, though, Tom Fool shall be that tyrant's
   death.

Bonaparte: Don't talk of fools, nor yet of death but learn this warlike dance,
For the time shall quickly come, when I am free in France.
Come on my bold hero.

Prince Bulow: Here am I, Prince Bulow from Flanders lately come,
Where the cannons they do rattle, and sound the warlike drum.
With my true courage, I follow Bony slow to your land to fight
For Bonaparte which is my whole delight.
Likewise you British dogs, I will defeat this night.

Duke of York: Here am I, the Duke of York, standing all on British land.
Proud Bonaparte I do defy, and all his daring band.
With British troops my boys, I went through Holland, France and Spain,
I will this night, with sword in hand, face Bonaparte again.

Prince Beelzebub: Here am I, Prince Beelzebub, Bonaparte's own true friend,
'Twas I did place ten votes to one, to make Bonaparte a king.
And when Bonaparte and I do meet, we'll lay our two heads together,
So take in hand, whate'er he will is my advice for ever.
Bonaparte was a fine scholar when he came to my school,
And 'twould take one of the best men in John Bull's troops, to make Bonaparte a fool.

Lord Wellington: Here am I, Lord Wellington, by the Duke of York
I fought full fifteen days, I killed and wounded with my broad sword that shines so bright.
When I was over in Flanders the other day
When I first began my warlike play,
I threw my guns into their flanks
To see my two brothers cut through their ranks.

I turned their front rank to the rear,
Although their army had been there
They turned their backs, and ran away.
And on their baggage we made our prey.
Now to Old England I am come,
You dirty French dogs shall have your doom,
And as for Beelzebub and Bonaparte this night
I'll cut them through the heart.

Prince Witsenberg: Here am I, Prince Witsenberg, come to your land to fight.
To fight for Bonaparte which is my true delight.
I will fight for Bonaparte as long as I am able, to make John Bull obey,
And when I can no longer stay, I'll turn my back, and run away.

Bonaparte: Behold, behold, my valiant soldiers are all come in,
Prepare for war, let us begin.
Form up your ranks, see all things clear,
And of these British rascals, never fear.

John Bull: Boys, be bold, but not too bold
Until these articles I do unfold.
Kill or be killed, no quarter give,
Don't suffer one of these dirty French dogs to live.

Tom Fool: To hit the first blow, Mr Bull, is half the battle,
Bonaparte's new fashioned dance, and John Bull's British rattle.

[They fight and John Bull falls.]

Tom Fool: Cheer up, cheer up my lads again,
The champion Bull he is not slain,
He's only fallen to rise again.
And I'm an Englishman, True Blue,
Will soon make Bonaparte to rue. To it again.

[They fight again, Bonaparte's soldiers run away and he tries to follow them, but Tom Fool stops him, saying:]

Tom Fool:	Proud Bonaparte, deliver thy sword unto me.
Bonaparte:	Alas, alas, where am I now?
Father Christmas:	Why, a prisoner atten [a taken]
John Bull:	Well done thou good and faithful servant Tom,
	A gold chain thou shalt have before tis long
	For saving me from that fatal blow.
	Ten thousand pounds is yours also.
	Besides a valiant soldier too.
Tom Fool:	Well Mr Bull, and what shall be done with the body of Bonaparte?
John Bull:	What's your proposal, Tom?
Tom Fool:	Take him through the towns and villages of England,
	And make a show of him.
John Bull:	No Tom, I have a letter in my pocket I had from Squire Greaves the other day,
	He wants an old horse for his dogs, so take him away.

[Bonaparte goes out, and comes back again with his men and addresses the British thus:]

Bonaparte:	Although you Britons thought to have me killed,
	Behold I come before you with all my men to yield.
	Although they were so scandalous as to run away,
	They come before your reverence to obey.

[They bow their heads.]

British Song:	
	So now we've gained the victory, we'll follow them with speed,
	For it never shall be said my boys, that Britons they do yield.
	We'll follow them and beat them, do all that we can do,
	For the bantam cock shall never crow on the Plains of Waterloo.
	We'll send him to some Island that is so far away,
	And we hope they will keep him there, for ever and a day.

And not let him return again, to do as he done before,
But keep him in some prison strong, and the wars will
soon be o'er.

So now unto old England we are returned again,
To drink to the health of Edward our King.
Likewise unto Lord Wellington, and all his armies too,
For if Bony lives for a hundred years, he'll remember
Waterloo.

Father Christmas: I should think he would remember such a time as that, I
should I know.

John Bull: Yes father, I should think he would, but I should think
you could sing us a song now.

Father Christmas: Well, I don't mind singing a song, only I must sit down
being old and stiff.

I had a lot of money, and I bought a little horse,
I bridled him and saddled him, and throwed my leg
across

[Chorus]   Wim Wam Waddle O, Jack stick straddle O,
Rossimo, Rossimo away went the broom.

So I had a little cow, and he had a little calf
I thought I had a bargain but I lost quite half.

So I sold my little cow, and bought a little dog,
A pretty little creature to keep off the mob.

So I sold my little dog, and bought a little cat,
A pretty little creature to keep off the rat.

So I sold my little cat, and bought a little goose,
He walked so many miles, his legs got loose.

So I sold my little goose, and bought a little duck,
He got into the mud, and there got stuck.

So I sold my little duck, and bought a little hare,
His hair came off, and he was bare.

So I sold my little hare, and bought a little rabbit,
I had to sell'm again, for he had a bad habit.

So I sold my little rabbit, and bought a little hen,
He laid so many eggs, that I couldn't mind when.

So I sold my little hen, and bought a little rat,
I had to sell'm again, for he got too fat.

So I sold my little rat, and bought a little mouse,
The fire on his tail, set fire to my house.

[Spoken.]   There my lads, what's think of that for a song?

John Bull: Awful row that, Father.
Father Christmas: Well thee make a better one then.
John Bull: The French are landed on the mountains high,
And we poor souls in the valleys do lie,
When General Wolfe to his men did say,
Come, come, my lads, and follow me.
The French are landed on the mountains high,
Through smoke and fire my boys,
Through smoke and fire my boys,
Tis by the noise of old England's cry.
The very first broadside we fired on them,
We killed and wounded five hundred men.
Well done, my lads, General Wolfe did say,
Brave lads of honour, Brave lads of honour,
Old England's sure to win the day.

The very first broadside they fired on us,
They wounded our General in his right breast,
See there he sits, but he cannot stand,
Fight on so boldly, Fight on so boldly,
For while I've life, I'll give command.

In the Eighteenth year, when we first began,

All for the honour of George our king.
So let all commanders do, as we have done before,
Be a soldiers friend my lads,
Be a soldiers friend my lads,
For they will fight for evermore.

In the yonder mountains, there lies my gold,
Take it and part it, for my blood's cold.
And when to old England you return,
Tell all my friends I'm dead and gone.
Pray tell my tender aged mother dear,
Weep not for me my friends,
Weep not for me my friends,
For I am going the Lord knows where.

Father Christmas: Yere, what's thee call that?
John Bull: A song father.
Father Christmas: Well, I do call it a horrible row, but I do want my horse
to go to market.
John Bull: Very well father, I suppose I had better get him.
Father Christmas: Yes, and see about it.

[John Bull goes out, and comes back leading the horse.]

Father Christmas: What's his name?
John Bull: Boll, father.
Father Christmas: Toll – I do see.
John Bull: No, Boll, father.
Father Christmas: Oh – I do see. Boll. Now let I go up top of him.

[The horse throws him off. He falls backwards saying:]

Father Christmas: Hullo, hullo, he very nearly killed I, now I'll kill he.
John Bull: Where's your horse, father?
Father Christmas: My horse; 40 mile away drownded in a dry ditch.
John Bull: That was a fine place to leave him father – You'd better
go back and look for him.

Father Christmas:	Will you help me?
John Bull:	Yes father, I'll help you.
Father Christmas:	Very well. Thee go that way, and I'll go this.

[Father Christmas falls over the horse.]

John Bull:	What's the matter father?
Father Christmas:	A great sea-bear, a great sea-bear.
John Bull:	Why tis your horse father.
Father Christmas:	No, my horse has got white legs.
John Bull:	So have this one father.
Father Christmas:	So he have – Well, what's the best thing to do?
John Bull:	Get a doctor father.
Father Christmas:	Well I s'pose I'd better go and look for one.
	Is there a doctor to be found?
	And to be had this night,
	To cure my poor little sucking colt,
	And make him stand upright?
Doctor:	Yes, father, there is a doctor to be found,
	And to be had this night—
	To cure your rip of a horse
	And make him stand upright.
Father Christmas:	What's that?
Doctor:	Sucking colt – father.
Father Christmas:	That do sound better. What's thy fee?
Doctor:	My fee is 40 pounds – ready money paid down.
	But since it's for your majesty, I'll only take 10 pounds.
Father Christmas:	That's a lot of money. What ca'st cure?
Doctor:	I can cure the hip, the pip, the palsy and the gout,
	Pains within and pains without.
	If old Harry's in your horse,
	I'll pretty quick turn him out again.
	I have a little bottle in my waistcoat pocket,
	Called the Golden Hospital —
	Touch nipper, napper, rise Jack,
	Make the crippled dame dance the monkey's hornpipe.
Father Christmas:	Thou dost talk a lot, what gwine to do for him?

Doctor:	Give him a ball, father.
Father Christmas:	Beat his head up against the wall, I'll soon do that.
Doctor:	No father, you'll kill him, if he's not dead already, give him a ball.
Father Christmas:	Oh! I do see, give him a ball then.
	Now then rise Boll. That isn't going to cure him. Now what gwine to do?
Doctor:	Bleed him father.
Father Christmas:	Where to?
Doctor:	In the eye vein.
Father Christmas:	Thee hold the knife, and I'll het en.
	Is that where these call the eye vein?
	Here's where I should call the eye win of he.
	Now then, rise Ball. That isn't going to cure him. Now what gwine to do?
Doctor:	Blow wind into him father.
Father Christmas:	Blow away then, blow away.
Doctor:	No you blow father. I'll watch the dust come out of his ears.
Father Christmas:	What, I do the work, and you have the money. Not very likely!
Doctor:	We'll go shares father.
Father Christmas:	Very well then.

[He blows three times, at the third time the horse rises, he tries to ride it again, but is thrown off, so he says to John Bull:]

Father Christmas:	Take him away.

[. . . John Bull comes back . . . John Bull and Bonaparte walk up and down with Father Christmas behind them.]

Servant Men:	We servant men have pleasure,
	Pastimes beyond measure.
	See the hare trip over the ground.

See the huntsman with his hounds,
As her drives them o'er the downs,
That's the pleasure of a servant man.

Father Christmas: I think my pleasure's better than all that,
I'se like to see my oxen grow up in great rolls of fat,
Travelling over the land so strong. I'se can reap, and I'se can mow,
I'se can plough and I'se can sow. I'se like to see the corn grow,
That's the pleasures for a whold husbandman.

Servant Men: We servant men do wear
Our livery fine and fair.
See the cockade in our hats, and the gold band all around.
Our shirt is white as milk, and our stockings fine as silk,
That's the raiment of a servant man.

Father Christmas: Don't thee tell I about silks and satins, that won't do for us to wear all through the bushes and briars. Give me a leather jacket and a pair of buckskin breeches, that's the raiment for a whold husbandman.

Servant Men: The servant men do eat all the very best of meat,
Such as cock, goose, cavern and swine.
After the lord and lady dine, we drink strong beer, ale or wine,
That's the diet of a servant man.

Father Christmas: Dost want to make me bad. Give I a hunch of bread and cheese, and a horn of whoam brewed ale, and a gad of bacon hung up in the chimney corner. That's the diet for an whold husbandman.

[All kneel round Father Christmas singing:]

Kind sir, we must confess, that your calling is the best,
And we give you the uttermost hand.
And evermore we pray, both by night and by day,
God bless the honest husbandman.

Father Christmas: That's I that is. I knowed these had to give in to one at
last. Now then, dress up there.

[He drills them, and they march round singing:]

> Our time is gone, we must be gone,
> We'll stay no longer here.
> God bless you all, both great and small,
> And send you a Happy New Year.

A Most Exciting Christmas

*Thomas Hardy, so affected by the mumming plays of his youth, harked
back to their formula in his last years for his wistfully autobiographical
retelling of the Tristan legend. The full title of this curious piece is* The
Famous Tragedy of the Queen of Cornwall at Tintagel in Lyonnesse: a
new version of an old story arranged as a play for mummers in one act,
requiring no theatre or scenery.
He also prepared a version of the traditional play, Saint George, *for a
group of Dorchester amateur actors, the Hardy Players, to perform in
their dramatization of* The Return of the Native *in 1920. Christmas Day
that year was a memorable occasion for everyone concerned. The local
newspaper, the* Dorset County Chronicle, *takes up the story.*

The Hardy Players visited the County Hospital on Christmas evening.
The party first sang the old Mellstock carols at the foot of the main
staircase. Then they gave in three of the wards the famous mummers play
which was a prominent feature of the recent performance of *The Return of
the Native*, and which was intensely enjoyed by the patients . . . After the
delightful entertainment by the Mummers, the hearts of all the patients were

cheered by the distribution of gifts by Father Christmas, realistically impersonated by Mr E.J. Stevens. He distributed his largesse with unstinted hand, and his geniality and merry quips were infectious. Further enjoyment was afforded by an excellent concert by the nurses . . .

Following their visit to the hospital the Players wended their way to Max Gate, and repeated the play as a tribute to Mr Hardy. Arriving at the house the Players first sang a carol, and when the last strains had died away the veteran author himself threw open the doors and with the utmost heartiness gave them the traditional welcome. The Players were invited to the drawing-room, and there before Mr and Mrs Hardy and a family party they gave the mumming scene, and, before such an audience, needless to say, played *con amore*, and Mr Hardy and his guests were delighted with the performance. The party were then invited by Mr and Mrs Hardy to 'a bite and a cup', and left amid an interchange of warmest appreciation and good wishes. The privilege of entertaining Mr Hardy under his own roof tree will be one of the Players' choicest memories.

And so it was. No fewer than three of the company later recorded in print their recollections of the evening, including Father Christmas (E.J. Stevens) and his daughter in the 1960s, and the Turkish Knight (Gertrude Bugler) in 1982. Gertrude Bugler's stunning performances as Eustacia Vye, and later as Tess, captivated the octogenarian Hardy (and aroused his wife's jealousy). Here is her vivid account of that unforgettable evening (prompted in places by the words of the master), as she relived it over sixty years later.

It was a beautiful starry night when we met at the end of Prince of Wales Road opposite the junction of South Street and South Walk. The company comprised the singers of the 1918 revival of the Mellstock Quire and the mummers who had taken part in Mr Tilley's adaptation of *The Return of the Native*, which was performed in November 1920. The singers carried an old horn lantern slung on a pole, and a violin or violins; the mummers were resplendent in their uniforms, helmets, and swords, with gay-coloured ribbons everywhere. Our strangely visored helmets had been made by Mr Tilley from directions and sketches made by Thomas Hardy, who attended several rehearsals, as did Florence and her dog Wessex.

So we laughed and chatted as we moved up Prince of Wales Road to the Wareham Road, and before long we were at the white gate which opened to

The Hardy Players in action. Gertrude Bugler is seated, second from left.

the short drive leading to the house. We crept up that drive in silence, and it seemed that all the lights of Max Gate welcomed us. The singers quietly grouped themselves round the lantern, and then, to use Hardy's own words, written so long before, there 'passed forth into the quiet night an ancient and time-worn hymn, embodying a quaint Christianity in words orally transmitted from father to son through several generations down to the present characters, who sang them out right earnestly'.

We were welcomed inside and shown where our stage was marked out by long strips of wood. Hardy at the rehearsal had suggested that we sang the words 'A-mumming we will go' as we entered, and again as we made our exit. He even hummed a tune for us, one we mostly knew as 'A-hunting we will go'; and of course we did just that. So we moved out to the porch in order to make what we hoped would be an impressive entrance. Father Christmas in his scarlet robe led the way with his huge club; then came the Valiant Soldier, the Turkish Knight, St George of England, and the Saracen. The Doctor in black, with his jar of 'alicampane' swinging from his waist, brought up the rear.

Father Christmas opened the play, saying:

> Here come I, old Father Christmas;
> Welcome or welcome not,
> I hope old Father Christmas
> Will never be forgot.
> Make room, make room, my gallant boys,
> And give us space to rhyme.
> We've come to show St George's play
> Upon this Christmas Time.

He swung his club, and stood with the Doctor at the back of the stage. The Valiant Soldier moved forward, saying 'Here come I, the Valiant Soldier, Slasher is my name', and so on. Eustacia (as the Turkish Knight) says:

> Here come I, a Turkish Knight,
> Who learnt in Turkish land to fight:
> I'll fight this man with courage bold;
> If his blood's hot, I'll make it cold.

Valiant Soldier replies, 'If then thou art the Turkish Knight, Draw out thy sword, and let us fight.' And fight they did, the issue of the combat being that the Valiant Soldier was slain by a preternaturally inadequate thrust from Eustacia, Jim coming down like a log.

The Turkish Knight then said he would fight St George and all his crew – 'Ay, country folk and warriors too'. St George entered magnificently with his well-known flourish,

> Here come I, St George, the valiant man
> With naked sword and spear in hand,
> Who fought the dragon
> And brought him to the slaughter,
> And by this won fair Sabra,
> The King of Egypt's daughter.
> What mortal men would dare to stand
> Before me with my sword in hand?

He and the Saracen fight. St George wins, but by now all the soldiers are on the ground, moaning and groaning. Father Christmas asks, 'Is there a doctor to be found. To cure me of this grievous wound?' 'Yes', says the Doctor and, after some bargaining over the price he is to be paid, he administers a few drops of the 'alicampane' to each fallen hero. The groans cease.

Our audience laughed heartily as we came to life. To the slow chanting of the Doctor and Father Christmas, we rose slowly from the dead in the awful manner required. (The chant was suggested by Thomas Hardy at our rehearsal; it happened to be 'Langdon in F', the favourite of Tess). With the points of their swords touching, the mummers then circled, singing right merrily, after their rapid recovery, 'And a-mumming we will go.' Our audience was most appreciative. We then moved to the dining-room for refreshments. As our visors were just coloured ribbons attached to the large helmets, our faces were obscured, and eating and drinking, made difficult . . .

So now seats were found for us all, and hosts and hostess came to talk with us, and to tell us how much they were enjoying the evening, as we were. There were recollections of *The Mellstock Quire*, *The Trumpet-Major*, rustic scenes from *The Dynasts*, and the crisis in the proposal scene of *The Return of the Native*, when the electric lighting in the Corn Exchange at Dorchester failed, and poor Clym and Eustacie had to sit in darkness on the stage till candles were brought. That had happened only a few weeks before, but tonight we could laugh even at that. Hardy was interested in everything, and could remember as much as we did. I was sitting with some of the older players when he came our way, and he had a word for everyone. When he came to me he said, 'Won't you raise your visor for me, Eustacia, as you did for Clym Yeobright?' So I held the ribbons aside as I had done for Clym, and saw a smiling Thomas Hardy.

On the following day, Boxing Day, Florence Hardy described the evening's events in a letter to a friend.

We, contrary to our usual custom, have spent a most exciting Christmas. Yesterday the Mummers (under our beloved Mr Tilley) came and performed in the drawing room here, to the intense joy of T.H. his brother and sister (whom I had here) and the rest of the household. And friends who accompanied them fiddled to us and sang carols outside – the real old Bockhampton carols. Then they came in had refreshments in the dining room and we had a very delightful time with them – Miss Bugler looking prettier than ever in her mumming dress. T.H. has lost his heart to her entirely, but as she is soon getting married I don't let that cast me down *too* much . . . Will you be able to see it [in London] do you think or will you come down here to see it with T.H. at Weymouth? We shall be delighted to see you here whenever you are able to come. T. is very well. At the party (of the Mummers etc) last night he was so gay – and one of them said to me that he had never seen him so young and happy and excited. He is now – this afternoon – writing a poem with great spirit: always a sign of well-being with him. Needless to say it is an intensely dismal poem.

Grammer's Shoes

William Barnes

Hardy set more than twenty poems, including two of his best loved, 'The Oxen' and 'The Darkling Thrush', against the background of Christmas and the New Year. This was partly because, as a working writer, he responded to magazine editors' calls for seasonal contributions; but a far more potent stimulus for an artist of his temperament was the cauldron of conflicting emotions which Christmas brought (and still brings) with it. Barnes, too, felt this emotional charge, but there was more honey, and less vinegar, in his nostalgic Christmas reflections.

I do seem to zee Grammer as she did use
Vor to show us, at Chris'mas, her wedden shoes,
An' her flat spreaden bonnet so big an' roun'
As a girt pewter dish a-turn'd upside down;
When we all did draw near
In a cluster to hear
O' the merry wold soul how she did use
To walk an' to dance wi' her high-heel shoes.

She'd a gown wi' girt flowers lik' hollyhocks,
An' zome stockens o' gramfer's a-knit wi' clocks,
An' a token she kept under lock an' key, —
A small lock ov his heair off avore 't wer grey.
An' her eyes wer red,
An' she shook her head,
When we'd all a-look'd at it, an' she did use
To lock it away wi' her wedden shoes.

She could tell us such teales about heavy snows,
An' o' rains an' o' floods when the waters rose
All up into the housen, an' carr'd awoy
All the bridge wi' a man an' his little bwoy;
An' o' vog an' vrost,
An' o' vo'k a-lost,
An' o' pearties at Chris'mas, when she did use
Vor to walk hwome wi' gramfer in high-heel shoes.

Ev'ry Chris'mas she lik'd vor the bells to ring,
An' to have in the zingers to hear em zing
The wold carols she heard many years a-gone,
While she warm'd em zome cider avore the bron';
An' she'd look an' smile
At our dancen, while
She did tell how her friends now a-gone did use
To reely wi' her in their high-heel shoes.

Ah! an' how she did like vor to deck wi' red
Holly-berries the window an' wold clock's head,
An' the clavy wi' boughs o' some bright green leaves,
An' to meake twoast an' eale upon Chris'mas eves;
But she's now, drough greace,
In a better pleace,
Though we'll never vorget her, poor soul, nor lose
Gramfer's token ov heair, nor her wedden shoes.

Burning the Holly

Thomas Hardy

Whereas Barnes celebrated the happy memories which accompanied Christmas, Hardy the great tragedian had learnt that the buffetings of ordinary life reveal themselves with greater intensity – greater poignancy – when silhouetted against a background of joyful celebration.

O you are sad on Twelfth Night,
I notice: sad on Twelfth Night;
You are as sad on Twelfth Night
As any that I know.

'Yes: I am sad on that night,
Doubtless I'm sad on that night:
Yes; I am sad on that night,
For we all loved her so!'

Why are you sad on Twelfth Night,
Especially on Twelfth Night?
Why are you sad on Twelfth Night
When wit and laughter flow?

—'She'd been a famous dancer,
Much lured of men; a dancer.
She'd been a famous dancer,
Facile in heel and toe . . . .

'And we were burning the holly
On Twelfth Night; the holly,
As people do: the holly,
Ivy, and mistletoe.

'And while it popped and crackled,
(She being our lodger), crackled;
And while it popped and crackled,
Her face caught by the glow,

'In he walked and said to her,
In a slow voice he said to her;
Yes, walking in he said to her,
"We sail before cock-crow."

'"Why did you not come on to me,
As promised? Yes, come on to me?
Why did you not come on to me,
Since you had sworn to go?"

'His eyes were deep and flashing,
As flashed the holm-flames: flashing;
His eyes were deep, and flashing
In their quick, keen upthrow.

'As if she had been ready,
Had furtively been ready;
As if she had been ready
For his insistence – lo!—

'She clasped his arm and went with him
As his entirely: went with him.
She clasped his arm and went with him
Into the sprinkling snow.

'We saw the prickly leaves waste
To ashes: saw the leaves waste;
The burnt-up prickly leaves waste . . . .
The pair had gone also.

—'On Twelfth Night, two years after—
Yes, Twelfth Night, two years after;

On Twelfth Night, two years after,
We sat – our spirits low –

'Musing, when back the door swung
Without a knock. The door swung;
Thought flew to her. The door swung,
And in she came, pale, slow;

'Against her breast a child clasped;
Close to her breast a child clasped;
She stood there with the child clasped,
Swaying it to and fro.

'Her look alone the tale told;
Quite wordless was the tale told;
Her careworn eyes the tale told
As larger they seemed to grow . . .

'One day next spring she disappeared,
The second time she disappeared.
And that time, when she'd disappeared
Came back no more. Ah, no!

'But we still burn the holly
On Twelfth Night; burn the holly
As people do: the holly,
Ivy, and mistletoe.'

Mrs Sibley and the Sexton

M.E. Francis

Anyone writing stories of Dorset life invites damning comparison with the works of the master, but this did not deter several others, famously, John Cowper Powys and John Meade Falkner. Further down the literary scale came spinners of melodramas and sentimental tales, such as Orme Angus, Evangeline Smith and Mary Blundell, who adopted the pen-name M.E. Francis. Here is part of one of her short stories, or 'idylls of country life', from a collection, Dorset Dear, *published in 1905. As a study of feminine guile employed to good effect at Christmas it is gently, but skilfully, written, and has a certain charm.*

The heroine, Mrs Sibley, is employed by the widowed sexton, John Foyle, to be his housekeeper and to look after his children. She, too, is widowed, her husband having recently died after some years in an asylum. Her matrimonial designs on her employer are discussed with a confidante, Martha Fry.

'Hasn't he said nothin' – nothin' at all?' inquired Mrs Fry, resting a plump hand on either knee and leaning forward.

'Not a single word,' replied her friend; 'that's to say, not a word wi' any sense in it. An' Sibley have been gone six months now, mind ye.'

'So he have!' replied Mrs Fry. 'An' ye mid say as you've been so good as a widder for nigh upon six year – ye mid indeed. A husband what's in the 'sylum is worse nor no husband at all. An' ye've a-been keepin' house for Foyle these four year, haven't ye?'

'Four year an' two month,' responded Mrs Sibley. 'There, the very day after Mrs Foyle were buried he did come to me an' he says so plain-spoke as anything, "Mrs Sibley," he says, "here be you a lone woman wi'out no family, an' here be I wi' all they little childern. Will 'ee come an' keep house for I an' look after 'em all? Ye'll not be the loser by it," says he. So I looks him straight in the face: "I bain't so sure o' that, Mr Foyle," I says. "I do look at it in this way, d'ye see. A woman has her chances," I says. "I don't think Sibley 'ull last so very long – they seldom does at the 'sylum – an' then here be I, a lone woman, as you do say. I mid very well like to settle myself again; an' if I go an' bury myself so far away from town in a place where there's sich a few neighbours, I don't see what prospects I'll have."'

'Well, that was straightforward enough,' commented Mrs Fry. 'He couldn't make no mistakes about your meanin'.'

'He could not,' agreed Mrs Sibley triumphantly; 'an' what's more, he didn't. He up an' spoke as plain as a man could speak. "Well, Mrs Sibley," he says, "there's a Fate what rules us all." He be always a-sayin' off bits o' po'try an' sichlike as he gets from the gravestones, ye know.'

'Ah,' remarked Mrs Fry nodding, 'being the sexton, of course, it do come nat'ral to 'en, don't it?'

'"There's a Fate what rules us all," he says,' resumed Mrs Sibley, '"an' we didn't ought to m'urn as if we had no hope. If you was a free 'ooman, Mrs Sibley – well, I'm a free man, and I'd make so good a husband as another. Maria did always find I so," he says.'

'Well, the man couldn't have said more.'

'So you'd think. But why don't he say summat now? There, I've a-kept his house an' seen arter his childern for more nor four year. Time's gettin' on, ye know; I bain't so young as I was.'

Mrs Fry began a polite disclaimer, but was overruled by the other.

'I bain't – tisn't in natur' as I could be. I wer' gettin' a bit anxious this year when poor Sibley did seem to be hangin' on so long, so I axed Rector to have 'en prayed for—.'

'A-h-h-h?' ejaculated Martha, as she paused. 'An' that did put the Lard in mind of 'en, I should think.'

'It did put the Lard in mind of 'en,' agreed Mrs Sibley with gusto. 'The Lard see'd he warn't no good to nobody in the 'sylum, as' so he wer' took.'

'An' Foyle have never come forward?' remarked Mrs Fry, after a significant pause.

'He've never made no offer, an' he've never said a single word to show he were thinkin' o' sich a thing. Not one word, Mrs Fry. I've given 'en the chance many a time . . . I says to 'en this marnin', "Mr Foyle," I says, "the

New Year's a-comin', an I think there ought to be some change in the early part of it for you an' me." "I don't want no changes," he says, "I'm very well satisfied as I be." I'm gettin' desperate, Mrs Fry.'

'Well, 'tis very onconsiderate,' returned Martha, 'very. I'm sure ye've said all ye could an' done all ye could. 'Tis hard, too, for a woman to have to go a-droppin' hints an' a-takin' the lead in such a delicate matter. I'm sure I don't know what to advise, my dear.'

After much deliberation, a plan is agreed. It is Christmas Eve, and before the family is sent to bed Mrs Sibley intimates to Mr Foyle that she proposes to leave the household the next day, and that he will have to find a new 'Auntie' for the children. They all take it rather badly.

'There, don't ye make such a fuss,' she remarked soothingly. 'Father's a bit upset; ye mustn't mind that. Get on with your teas, dears. There, ye may have a bit of jam to it to-night, as it's Christmas Eve; and afterwards we'll stick up some green, and you must all hang up your stockin's and see what you'll find there in the marnin'.'

Cheerfulness was immediately restored; little faces grimed by tears smiled afresh; plates were extended for plentiful helpings of blackberry jam, and soon little tongues were gleefully discussing the morrow's prospects, and particularly the treasures which might be looked for in the stockings . . . As the children retired for the night, Henery paused beside her for a moment.

'You won't truly go to-morrow, Auntie?' he pleaded coaxingly.

Mrs Sibley paused a moment, and in the interval the sound of the sexton's slouching step was heard without, and his hand fumbled at the latch.

'It do all depend on Father, Henery,' said Mrs Sibley, raising her voice slightly. 'He do know very well as I do want a change.'

Mr Foyle entered, looking weary and depressed, and sat down in his customary chair. Mrs Sibley cast a searching glance round the kitchen, and, possessing herself of a pair of spotted china dogs which adorned the mantel-piece, added them to her collection, and retired.

The sexton lit his pipe, and had been smoking in gloomy silence for some time, when Mrs Sibley re-entered. Going to the dresser, and opening a drawer, she abstracted a number of oranges, nuts, crackers, and other such wares, and filled her apron with them.

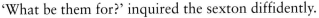
'What be them for?' inquired the sexton diffidently.

'Why, they be surprises for the childern,' returned she.

'Ah,' rejoined John Foyle, 'surprises, be they?'

'Yes,' said Mrs Sibley, 'they do look for 'em reg'lar, they do. I always fill their stockin's wi' 'em every Christmas.'

'Oh,' said the sexton, 'put their surprises in their stockin's, do 'ee?'

Mrs Sibley nodded and withdrew, leaving John sunk in profound thought.

'This 'ere be a vale o' tears,' he remarked presently, as he knocked the ashes out of his pipe. He rose, went to the table, turned up the lamp a little more, and fetching pen, ink, and paper from the window-sill on which they usually reposed, sat down to indite a letter. It cost him much labour and thought, but, after all, it was a brief enough document. When completed it ran thus: 'If Mrs Sibley will meet Mr Foyle in the churchyard to-morrow morning about nine o'clock when nobody's about she will hear of something to your advantage. Yours truly, John Foyle.'

'I couldn't,' said the sexton to himself, 'put the question in any sort of public way. The childern is in and out, and the neighbours mid pop in. The churchyard is best and most nat'ral.'

He folded the letter, put it in an envelope, and addressed it; then, looking round, descried hanging over a chair-back one of Mrs Sibley's stockings. 'The very thing!' exclaimed John. 'The Christmas surprises do always go in stockin's. It'll be a surprise for she, I d' 'low – not but what she didn't look for it,' he added with a grim chuckle.

He placed the letter in the stocking, fastened it securely with a loop of string, and, going cautiously upstairs, slung it over Mrs Sibley's door-handle. He paused a moment, winking to himself, and then made his way on tiptoe to his own room.

Next morning, in the churchyard, it is Mrs Sibley's turn to play hard-to-get.

He descried a tall figure in black making its way, not towards him, but towards that portion of the churchyard wherein reposed the mortal remains of the lamented Mr Sibley. After some hesitation the sexton followed, and Mrs Sibley, having deposited a wreath of evergreens on the grave, turned round with a mournful expression.

'At such times as these, Mr Foyle,' she remarked, 'the mind do nat'rally feel m'urnfull.'

'True, true!' agreed the sexton uncomfortably.

'He was a good husband, Mr Foyle,' said the widow in a melancholy tone.

'To be sure,' said John doubtfully.

'I shall never look upon his like again,' resumed Mrs Sibley, shaking her head.

The sexton glanced from her disconsolate face to the wreath of evergreens, and then back again. Mrs Sibley was still shaking her head with an air of gentle resignation.

'I think I'll be goin',' said Mr Foyle with sudden desperation. 'I thought you did step out to this 'ere churchyard with another intention.'

Mrs Sibley glanced at him in mild surprise.

'Ye didn't chance to get no letter this marnin', I s'pose?' continued the sexton with some heat.

'A letter!' repeated Mrs Sibley.

'E-es, the letter what I did put in your stockin' for a surprise,' added John emphatically.

Mrs Sibley's melancholy vanished as by magic; she smiled on the sexton, not only affably, but positively coyly.

'An' it was a surprise!' she exclaimed, 'it was indeed. E-es, Mr Foyle.'

She paused again, and then, all scruples apparently vanquished by the delicacy of John's attitude, she extended a bony hand from beneath the folds of her black shawl.

'That's why I'm here,' she said.

One Who Married Above Him

Thomas Hardy

Smouldering resentments and unseen tensions within families all too often reveal themselves at Christmas, when normal patterns of life are suspended and expectations forlornly aroused. We, at the end of the twentieth century, may feel that this is our peculiar crisis, engendered by the saccharin juggernaut which we inflict on ourselves each winter. But we have only inherited an age-old problem, and Hardy depicted it in this curiously wrought vignette of a flawed marriage. Like 'Burning the Holly', it is a product of his last, reflective, years; it was published in 1925.

''Tis you, I think? Back from your week's work, Steve?'

'It is I. Back from work this Christmas Eve.'

'But you seem off again? – in this night-rime?'

'I am off again, and thoroughly off this time.'

'What does that mean?'

'More than may first be seen . . .

Half an hour ago I footed homeward here,
No wife found I, nor child, nor maid, indoors or near.
She has, as always, gone with them to her mother's at the farm,
Where they fare better far than here, and, maybe, meet less harm.
She's left no fire, no light, has cooked me nothing to eat,
Though she had fuel, and money to get some Christmas meat.

Christmas with them is grand, she knows, and brings good victual,
Other than how it is here, where it's but lean and little.
But though not much, and rough,
If managed neat there's enough.
She and hers are too highmade for me;
But she's whimmed her once too often, she'll see!
Farmer Bollen's daughter should never have married a man that's poor;
And I can stand it no longer; I'm leaving; you'll see me no more, be sure.'

'But nonsense: you'll be back again 'ere bedtime, and lighting a fire,
And sizzling your supper, and vexing not that her views of supper are
  higher.'

'Never for me.'

'Well, we shall see.'

The sceptical neighbour and Stephen then followed their foredesigned
  ways,
And their steps dimmed into white silence upon the slippery glaze;
And the trees went on with their spitting amid the icicled haze.

The evening whiled, and the wife with the babies came home,
But he was not there, nor all Christmas Day did he come.
Christmastide went, and likewise went the New Year,
But no husband's footfall revived,
And month after month lapsed, graytime to green and to sere,
And other new years arrived,
And the children grew up: one husbanded and one wived. —
She wept and repented,
But Stephen never relented.
And there stands the house, and the sycamore-tree and all,
With its roots forming steps for the passers who care to call,
And there are the mullioned windows, and Ham-Hill door,
Through which Steve's wife was brought out, but which Steve re-entered
  no more.

The Stranger at the Party

T h o m a s   H a r d y

The awesome destructive power of tangled emotions is a recurrent theme throughout Hardy's work. Death is an unwelcome guest at Christmas, not only stalking poems such as 'The Rash Bride' (where a young wife, hearing the carollers, throws herself down a well); it is present too in one of the short stories, The Grave at the Handpost, *where a suicide is buried on Christmas Eve. And, most memorably, violent death visits Mr Boldwood's Christmas party, as* Far From the Madding Crowd *reaches its electrifying climax.*

Troy confronts Boldwood. Helen Allingham's illustration for the Cornhill Magazine *serialization of* Far from the Madding Crowd, *December 1874.*

The party has been interrupted by the arrival of a stranger, Sergeant Troy, who has come to clutch his wife, Bathsheba, from the rival attentions of Boldwood.

Boldwood was among those who did not notice that he was Troy. 'Come in, come in!' he repeated, cheerfully, 'and drain a Christmas beaker with us, stranger!'

Troy next advanced into the middle of the room, took off his cap, turned down his coat-collar, and looked Boldwood in the face. Even then Boldwood did not recognize that the impersonator of Heaven's persistent irony towards him, who had once before broken in upon his bliss, scourged him, and snatched his delight away, had come to do these things a second time. Troy began to laugh a mechanical laugh: Boldwood recognized him now.

Troy turned to Bathsheba. The poor girl's wretchedness at this time was beyond all fancy or narration. She had sunk down on the lowest stair; and there she sat, her mouth blue and dry, and her dark eyes fixed vacantly upon him, as if she wondered whether it were not all a terrible illusion.

Then Troy spoke. 'Bathsheba, I come here for you!'

She made no reply.

'Come home with me: come!'

Bathsheba moved her feet a little, but did not rise. Troy went across to her.

'Come, madam, do you hear what I say?' he said, peremptorily.

A strange voice came from the fireplace – a voice sounding far off and confined, as if from a dungeon. Hardly a soul in the assembly recognized the thin tones to be those of Boldwood. Sudden despair had transformed him.

'Bathsheba, go with your husband!'

Nevertheless, she did not move. The truth was that Bathsheba was beyond the pale of activity – and yet not in a swoon. She was in a state of mental *gutta serena*; her mind was for the minute totally deprived of light at the same time that no obscuration was apparent from without.

Troy stretched out his hand to pull her towards him, when she quickly shrank back. This visible dread of him seemed to irritate Troy, and he seized her arm and pulled it sharply. Whether his grasp pinched her, or whether his mere touch was the cause, was never known, but at the moment of his seizure she writhed, and gave a quick, low scream.

The scream had been heard but a few seconds when it was followed by a sudden deafening report that echoed through the room and stupefied them all. The oak partition shook with the concussion, and the place was filled with grey smoke.

In bewilderment they turned their eyes to Boldwood. At his back, as he stood before the fireplace, was a gun-rack, as is usual in farmhouses, constructed to hold two guns. When Bathsheba had cried out in her husband's grasp, Boldwood's face of gnashing despair had changed. The veins had swollen, and a frenzied look had gleamed in his eye. He had turned quickly, taken one of the guns, cocked it, and at once discharged it at Troy.

Troy fell. The distance apart of the two men was so small that the charge of shot did not spread in the least, but passed like a bullet into his body. He uttered a long guttural sigh – there was a contraction – an extension – then his muscles relaxed, and he lay still.

Old Christmas Eve

Francis Kilvert

The Christmases of the First World War were probably the most cheerless of Hardy's life, because then death and destruction were no longer ingredients in the novelist's store, but stark everyday truths. In a letter to a clergyman friend, dated Christmas Day 1914, he wrote: 'A newspaper editor asked me to send him a Christmas greeting for his readers, and I told him that the puzzle was too hard for me, seeing that present times are an absolute negation of Christianity.' And in his autobiography he confided that the war had destroyed all his belief in the gradual ennoblement of man, or of any 'fundamental ultimate Wisdom' at the back of things.

During the second year of that terrible war, insignificiantly at the foot of a column of an inside page of The Times *on Christmas Eve, was first published 'The Oxen', a short poem which has become one of*

the best known that Hardy ever wrote. It is constructed about the
widespread belief that animals at Christmas possessed supernatural
powers or assumed human characteristics, which was often coupled
with a notion that only certain people had the ability to witness such a
miracle.
A moving example of such a belief, sincerely held, is recorded in the
diary of Francis Kilvert in January 1878. Kilvert was an exact
contemporary of Hardy – both were born in 1840 – but his literary
career took a very different course. In 1878 he was a clergyman in a
remote region of the Welsh borderland, and had only another year of life
ahead of him. Those of his diaries which were not destroyed lay
undiscovered for a further sixty years, and were not published until long
after Hardy's death. So the poet would not have been aware of this
version, told to Kilvert by an elderly lady, Priscilla Price, in her cottage
on the hill above Bredwardine, when he visited her on 'Old' Christmas
Eve, 5 January.

Speaking of the blowing of the Holy Thorn and the kneeling and sweeping of the oxen on old Christmas Eve (to-night) Priscilla said, 'I have known old James Meredith forty years and I have never known him far from the truth, and I said to him one day, "James, tell me the truth, did you ever see the oxen kneel on old Christmas Eve at the Weston?" And he said, "No, I never saw them kneel at the Weston but when I was at Hinton at Staunton-on-Wye I saw them. I was watching them on old Christmas Eve and at 12 o'clock the oxen that were standing knelt down upon their knees and those that were lying down rose up on their knees and there they stayed kneeling and moaning, and tears running down their faces."'

'Tis Quite True, Sir

T h o m a s   H a r d y

A similar belief, of course, existed in Dorset, and Hardy knew of it long before 1915. According to his wife it was Jemima Hardy, his mother, who had told it to him. In Tess of the d'Urbervilles, *written twenty-five years earlier, he had used it to comic effect.*

'Oh yes; there's nothing like a fiddle,' said the dairyman. 'Though I do think that bulls are more moved by a tune than cows – at least that's my experience. Once there was a old aged man over at Mellstock – William Dewy by name – one of the family that used to do a good deal of business as tranters over there, Jonathan, do ye mind ? – I knowed the man by sight as well as I know my own brother, in a manner of speaking. Well, this man was a coming home-along from a wedding where he had been playing his fiddle, one fine moonlight night, and for shortness' sake he took a cut across Forty-acres, a field lying that way, where a bull was out to grass. The bull seed William, and took after him, horns aground, begad; and though William runned his best, and hadn't much drink in him (considering 'twas a wedding, and the folks well off), he found he'd never reach the fence and get over in time to save himself. Well, as a last thought, he pulled out his fiddle as he runned, and struck up a jig, turning to the bull, and backing towards the corner. The bull softened down, and stood still, looking hard at William Dewy, who fiddled on and on; till a sort of a smile stole over the bull's face. But no sooner did William stop his playing and turn to get over hedge than the bull would stop his smiling and lower his horns towards the seat of William's breeches. Well, William had to turn about and play on, willy-nilly; and 'twas only three o'clock in the world, and 'a knowed that nobody would come that way for hours, and he so leery and tired that 'a didn't know what to do. When he had scraped till about four o'clock he felt that he verily would have to give over soon, and he said to himself, "There's only this last tune between me and eternal welfare! Heaven save me, or I'm a done man." Well, then he called to mind how he'd seen the cattle kneel o' Christmas Eves in the dead o' night. It was not Christmas Eve then, but it came into his head to play a trick upon the bull. So he broke into the 'Tivity Hymn, just as at Christmas carol-singing; when, lo and behold, down went the bull on his bended knees, in his ignorance, just as if 'twere the true 'Tivity night and hour. As soon as his horned friend were down, William turned, clinked off like a long-dog, and jumped safe over hedge, before the praying bull had got on his feet again to take after him. William used to say that he'd seen a man look a fool a good many times, but never such a fool as that bull looked when he found his pious feelings had been played upon, and 'twas not Christmas Eve . . . Yes, William Dewy, that was the man's name; and I can tell you to a foot where's he a-lying in Mellstock Churchyard at this very moment – just between the second yew-tree and the north aisle.'

'It's a curious story; it carries us back to mediaeval times, when faith was a living thing!'

The remark, singular for a dairy-yard, was murmured by the voice behind the dun cow; but as nobody understood the reference no notice was taken, except that the narrator seemed to think it might imply scepticism as to his tale.

'Well, 'tis quite true, sir, whether or no. I knowed the man well.'

'Oh yes; I have no doubt of it,' said the person behind the dun cow.

Cross-in-Hand Stone

Henry Moule

Folklore collectors, like Hardy himself, introduced a note of scepticism to such legends. Henry Moule, who was the curator of the Dorset County Museum in Dorchester, and a friend of Hardy, published a variant of the story in 1889, attached to a standing stone overlooking Blackmore Vale in north Dorset. The stone features in Tess, *as the spot where the heroine meets Alec d'Urberville and is persuaded to swear on the stone that she will never tempt him. Hardy described the scene as 'something sinister, or solemn, according to mood', and later based his poem 'The Lost Pyx' on its legend.*

On Batcombe Down, Dorset, is a stone about three feet high, evidently part of a cross, and called Cross [in] Hand Stone. Why should a cross be set up, away there on the down? Well, this 'be teale twold o't'. Back in the middle ages, one dark, wild winter night, Batcombe priest was sent for to take the viaticum to a dying man, two or three miles off. Taking pyx and service-book, he sallied out with a brave heart on his dark, lonely way over Batcombe Down, and safely reached the sick man's house. But on getting in, and producing what was needed for his ministration – where was the pyx? It was lost. He had dropped it on the way, and its fall on the turf of Batcombe Down – in the howling wind too! – had not been heard. Back he toiled, into the darkness and the storm, on his almost hopeless quest. Hopeless? The easiest search ever made. Up on Batcombe Down there was a pillar of fire, reaching from heaven to earth, and steadily shining in the storm. What could this be? He struggled on faster and faster, with strange, half-formed hopes. He came near to the spot over which stood the calm beam in the gale. He saw numbers of cattle of various kinds, gathered in a circle – kneeling – kneeling round the pyx.

Well, this seemed to me to be the mediaeval legend, rendering a reason for Batcombe Cross being set up there, away on the down, where, though time-worn, it yet remains. But (*me judice*) in the last century a rider was added, as follows:

The priest was much astounded at what he saw, yet not so much so but that he observed among the live-stock a black horse, kneeling, indeed, like the rest, but only on one knee. The priest said to this lukewarm beast, 'Why don't you kneel on both knees, like the rest ?' 'Wouldn't kneel at all if I could help it.' 'Who, then, are you ?' 'The devil.' 'Why do you take the form of a horse?' 'So that men may steal me and get hung, and I get hold of them. Got three or four already.'

The Cross-in-Hand Stone, Batcombe Down. Visitors still place votive small change on top of the monolith.

Hoping It Might Be So

Thomas Hardy

*It is strange that Hardy's poem 'The Oxen' should have become such a
favourite at church carol services because, like the legend of the lost pyx,
the Devil creeps in at the end. The Devil in this case is Hardy's
disillusioned agnosticism. By 1915 the First World War has destroyed
his belief in Christmas miracles ('so fair a fancy few believe in these
years'), and left him a reluctant unbeliever who can only ponder the
naïvety of his youth.*

Christmas Eve, and twelve of the clock.
'Now they are all on their knees,'
An elder said as we sat in a flock
By the embers in hearthside ease.

We pictured the meek mild creatures where
They dwelt in their strawy pen,
Nor did it occur to one of us there
To doubt that they were kneeling then.

So fair a fancy few would weave
In these years! Yet, I feel,
If someone said on Christmas Eve,
'Come; see the oxen kneel

'In the lonely barton by yonder coomb
Our childhood used to know,'
I should go with him in the gloom,
Hoping it might be so.

The Mellstock Club

When those words were written the war had another three years to run its course. And in the wake of its ending a natural desire arose in communities everywhere to commemorate the sacrifices which it had demanded. At Stinsford the war memorial took the form of a reading room which, as the Dorset County Chronicle *reported, was opened in December 1919.*

STINSFORD. GENEROUS GIFT TO THE PARISH

A fully-equipped club and reading-room has been given to the parish by Mr Cecil Hanbury of Kingston Park as a memorial to Stinsford men who fell and served in the war. It was peculiarly fitting that the opening ceremony should have been performed by Mr Thomas Hardy, OM, who has invested the village of 'Melstock' with so much romance in his famous book Under the Greenwood Tree. There was a large gathering in the room, which was tastefully decorated, the only drawback to the complete success of the ceremony being the unavoidable absence of the generous donor, who had a previous engagement at Longburton . . . An enjoyable dance followed. It was mentioned by Mr Hardy that the room was erected on the site of a cottage known in days gone by as 'Jacob's Joy', and where weekly village dances used to be held.

Annoyance at being misreported (and Mellstock being misspelled) may underlie Hardy's decision to quote verbatim in his autobiography the speech which he made on this occasion, explaining caustically that it had not been reported in any newspaper. After a wry comment on the intended name for the building, The Mellstock Club, he told anecdotes about the history of the village, and then turned to reminiscences.

Then there used to be dancing parties at Christmas, and some weeks after. This kind of party was called a Jacob's Join, in which every guest contributed a certain sum to pay the expenses of the entertainment – it was mostly half-a-crown in this village. They were very lively parties I believe. The curious thing is that the man who used to give the house-room for the dances lived in the cottage which stood exactly where this Club house stands now – so that when you dance here you will be simply carrying on the tradition of the spot.

The man in question, as the autobiography explains, was Robert Reason, the village shoemaker, who was the original for Robert Penny, a member of the Mellstock Quire. Reason had died nearly a century earlier, on Boxing Day 1819, and more than twenty years before Hardy was born. Other members of the quire were modelled on men he had known from childhood, his own father (also Thomas Hardy), and his neighbours James Dart and William Keats the tranter (or carrier). But their weekly duty as musicians in the gallery at Stinsford Church, and their annual carolling around the parish through the early hours of Christmas morning, had come to an end very soon after the novelist's birth, so that his descriptions of their activities were based on vigorous family traditions, and not on personal recollection.

The Humstrum

William Barnes

The Mellstock Quire takes centre stage in the early chapters of Under the Greenwood Tree. *They and other bands of village musicians also appear in a number of poems, as we shall see, practising psalms at the beginning of* Two on a Tower, *and in two of the stories known collectively as* A Few Crusted Characters. *But as with many other aspects of Dorset rural life, Hardy's depiction was anticipated by his mentor, the poet William Barnes.*

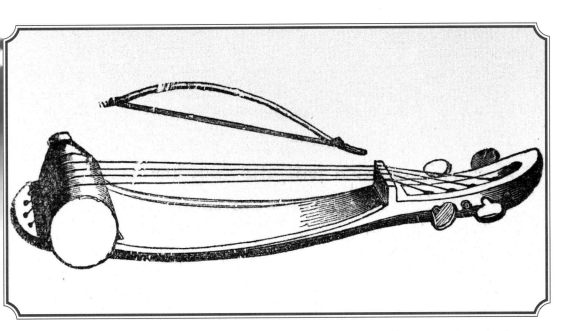

The Humstrum. Engraving by William Barnes for the 1869 edition of his Poems of Rural Life
in the Dorset Dialect.

Why woonce, at Chris'mas-tide, avore
The wold year wer a-reckon'd out,
The humstrums here did come about,
A-sounden up at ev'ry door.
But now a bow do never screape
A humstrum, any where all round,
An' zome can't tell a humstrum's sheape,
An' never heard his jinglen sound,
As *ing-an-ing* did ring the string,
As *ang-an-ang* the wires did clang.

The strings a-tighten'd lik' to crack
Athirt the canister's tin zide,
Did reach, a-glitt'ren, zide by zide,
Above the humstrum's hollow back.
An' there the bwoy, wi' bended stick,

A-strung wi' heair, to meake a bow,
Did dreve his elbow, light'nen quick,
Athirt the strings vrom high to low,
As *ing-an-ing* did ring the string,
As *ang-an-ang* the wires did clang.

The mother there did stan' an' hush
Her child, to hear the jinglen sound,
The merry maid, a-scrubben round
Her white-steav'd pail, did stop her brush.
The mis'ess there, vor wold time's seake,
Had gifts to gi'e, and smiles to show,
An' measter, too, did stan' an' sheake
His two broad zides, a-chucklen low,
While *ing-an-ing* did ring the string,
While *ang-an-ang* the wires did clang.

The players' pockets wer a-strout,
Wi' wold brown pence, a-rottlen in,
Their zwangen bags did soon begin,
Wi' brocks an' scraps, to plim well out.
The childern all did run an' poke
Their heads vrom hatch or door, an' shout
A-runnen back to wolder vo'k,
'Why, here! the humstrums be about!'
As *ing-an-ing* did ring the string,
As *ang-an-ang* the wires did clang.

An Introduction to the Quire

Thomas Hardy

*The era of the church musicians, who were everywhere displaced from
their galleries by those ogres of Victorian sophistication, the harmonium
and the barrel-organ, was fading in the memories of Hardy's readers by
the time that* Under the Greenwood Tree *appeared in 1872. By 1896,
when Hardy prefaced a new edition, he felt the need to introduce his
musicians to new generations of readers in three beautifully crafted
paragraphs of social history.*

The zest of these bygone instrumentalists must have been keen and
staying to take them, as it did, on foot every Sunday after a toilsome
week, through all weathers, to the church, which often lay at a distance
from their homes. They usually received so little in payment for their
performances that their efforts were really a labour of love. In the parish I
had in my mind when writing the present tale, the gratuities received yearly
by the musicians at Christmas were somewhat as follows: From the manor-
house ten shillings and a supper; from the vicar ten shillings; from the
farmers five shillings each; from each cottage-household one shilling;
amounting altogether to not more than ten shillings a head annually – just
enough, as an old executant told me, to pay for their fiddle-strings, repairs,
rosin, and music-paper (which they mostly ruled themselves). Their music in
those days was all in their own manuscript, copied in the evenings after
work, and their music-books were home-bound.

It was customary to inscribe a few jigs, reels, horn-pipes, and ballads in
the same book, by beginning it at the other end, the insertions being
continued from front and back till sacred and secular met together in the
middle, often with bizarre effect, the words of some of the songs exhibiting
that ancient and broad humour which our grandfathers, and possibly
grandmothers, took delight in, and is in these days unquotable.

Hardy's own illustration of church musicians, from his architectural notebook.

The aforesaid fiddle-strings, rosin, and music-paper were supplied by a pedlar, who travelled exclusively in such wares from parish to parish, coming to each village about every six months. Tales are told of the consternation once caused among the church fiddlers when, on the occasion of their producing a new Christmas anthem, he did not come to time, owing

Roger Trim (left) playing Hardy's violin, and Nick Thomas playing Hardy's father's violin, beneath the newly reconstructed west gallery in Stinsford Church, 1997.

to being snowed up on the downs, and the straits they were in through having to make shift with whipcord and twine for strings. He was generally a musician himself, and sometimes a composer in a small way, bringing his own new tunes, and tempting each choir to adopt them for a consideration. Some of these compositions which now lie before me, with their repetitions of lines, half-lines, and half-words, their fugues and their intermediate symphonies, are good singing still, though they would hardly be admitted into such hymn-books as are popular in the churches of fashionable society at the present time.

Going the Rounds

Thomas Hardy

Under the Greenwood Tree begins with the members of the Mellstock Quire making their way on Christmas Eve to the house of the tranter, Reuben Dewy, for the essential preliminaries – cider, and in a lesser degree, practice – to the impending night's carolling.

'Better try over number seventy-eight before we start, I suppose?' said William, pointing to a heap of old Christmas-carol books on a side table.

'Wi' all my heart,' said the choir generally.

'Number seventy-eight was always a teaser – always. I can mind him ever since I was growing up a hard boy-chap.'

'But he's a good tune, and worth a mint o' practice,' said Michael.

'He is; though I've been mad enough wi' that tune at times to seize en and tear en all to linnit. Ay, he's a splendid carrel – there's no denying that.'

'That first line is well enough,' said Mr Spinks; 'but when you come to "O, thou man," you make a mess o't.'

'We'll have another go into en, and see what we can make of the martel. Half-an-hour's hammering at en will conquer the toughness of en; I'll warn it.'

A little more practice ensues, a good deal more cider, and a diversion into the intriguing shape of the young schoolmistress's shoe (crucial to the plot later on).

Shortly after ten o'clock the singing-boys arrived at the tranter's house, which was invariably the place of meeting, and preparations were made for the start. The older men and musicians wore thick coats, with stiff perpendicular collars, and coloured handkerchiefs wound round and round the neck till the end came to hand, over all which they just showed their ears and noses, like people looking over a wall. The remainder, stalwart ruddy men and boys, were dressed mainly in snow-white smock-frocks, embroidered upon the shoulders and breasts, in ornamental forms of hearts, diamonds, and zig-zags. The cider-mug was emptied for the ninth time, the music-books were

~~The Mellstock Quire~~
or
Under the Greenwood Tree.
A rural painting of the Dutch School.

Part I. Winter.
Chapter I
Mellstock Lane.

To dwellers in a wood, almost every species of tree has its voice as well as its feature. At the passing of the breeze the fir-trees sob & moan no less distinctly than they rock: the holly whistles as it battles with itself: the ash hisses amid its quivering: the beech rustles as its flat boughs rise & fall. And winter, which modifies the notes of such trees as shed their leaves does not destroy their individuality.

On a cold & starry Christmas-eve, not less than a generation ago a man was passing along a lane in the darkness of a plantation that whispered thus distinctively to his intelligence. All the evidences of his nature were those afforded by the spirit of his footsteps which succeeded each other lightly & quickly, & by the liveliness of his voice as he sang in a rural cadence ... "— With the rose & the lily
And the daffodowndilly,
The lads & the lasses a-sheep-shearing go."

The first page of Hardy's autograph of Under the Greenwood Tree, *completed in 1871, and now in the Dorset County Museum.*

arranged, and the pieces finally decided upon. The boys in the meantime put the old horn-lanterns in order, cut candles into short lengths to fit the lanterns; and, a thin fleece of snow having fallen since the early part of the evening, those who had no leggings went to the stable and wound wisps of hay round their ankles to keep the insidious flakes from the interior of their boots.

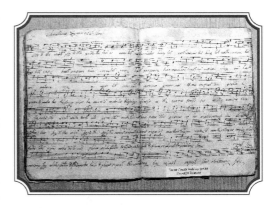

A page of a manuscript carol book which belonged to James Saunders of Puddletown in 1835. This carol was composed by Thomas Shoel of Montacute, in Somerset, a talented and locally well-known village poet, who had the distinction of being commemorated in an essay by Llewelyn Powys.

Mellstock was a parish of considerable acreage, the hamlets composing it lying at a much greater distance from each other than is ordinarily the case. Hence several hours were consumed in playing and singing within hearing of every family, even if but a single air were bestowed on each. There was Lower Mellstock, the main village; half a mile from this were the church and vicarage, and a few other houses, the spot being rather lonely now, though in past centuries it had been the most thickly-populated quarter of the parish. A mile north-east lay the hamlet of Upper Mellstock, where the tranter lived; and at other points knots of cottages, besides solitary farmsteads and dairies.

Old William Dewy, with the violoncello, played the bass; his grandson Dick the treble violin; and Reuben and Michael Mail the tenor and second violins respectively. The singers consisted of four men and seven boys, upon whom devolved the task of carrying and attending to the lanterns, and holding the books open for the players. Directly music was the theme, old William ever and instinctively came to the front.

'Now mind, neighbours,' he said, as they all went out one by one at the door, he himself holding it ajar and regarding them with a critical face as they passed, like a shepherd counting out his sheep. 'You two counter-boys, keep your ears open to Michael's fingering, and don't ye go straying into the treble part along o' Dick and his set, as ye did last year; and mind this especially when we be in "Arise, and hail." Billy Chimlen, don't you sing quite so raving mad as you fain would; and, all o'ye, whatever ye do, keep from making a

MICHAEL MAIL.

*Michael Mail, by R. Knights, for the 1878
illustrated edition of* Under the Greenwood Tree.

great scuffle on the ground when we go in at people's gates; but go quietly, so as to strike up all of a sudden, like spirits.'

'Farmer Ledlow's first?'

'Farmer Ledlow's first; the rest as usual.'

'And, Voss,' said the tranter terminatively, 'you keep house here till about half-past two; then heat the metheglin and cider in the warmer you'll find turned up upon the copper; and bring it wi' the victuals to church-hatch, as th'st know.'

At midnight they set out across the snow, and by two o'clock they have visited most of the outlying parts of the parish. As they trudge back they pass their time arguing the merits of various musical instruments.

By this time they were crossing to a gate in the direction of the school, which, standing on a slight eminence at the junction of three ways, now rose in unvarying and dark flatness against the sky. The instruments were retuned, and all the band entered the school enclosure, enjoined by old William to keep upon the grass.

'Number seventy-eight,' he softly gave out as they formed round in a semicircle, the boys opening the lanterns to get a clearer light, and directing their rays on the books.

Then passed forth into the quiet night an ancient and timeworn hymn, embodying a quaint Christianity in words orally transmitted from father to son through several generations down to the present characters, who sang them out right earnestly:

Going the Rounds, by R. Knights, for the 1878 illustrated edition of Under the Greenwood Tree.

'Remember Adam's fall,
O thou Man:
Remember Adam's fall
From Heaven to Hell . . .

Having concluded the last note, they listened for a minute or two, but found that no sound issued from the schoolhouse.

'Four breaths, and then, "O, what unbounded goodness!" number fifty-nine,' said William.

This was duly gone through, and no notice whatever seemed to be taken of the performance.

'Good guide us, surely 'tisn't a' empty house, as befell us in the year thirty-nine and forty-three!' said old Dewy.

'Perhaps she's jist come from some musical city, and sneers at our doings?' the tranter whispered.

"Od rabbit her!' said Mr Penny, with an annihilating look at a corner of the school chimney, 'I don't quite stomach her, if this is it. Your plain music well done is as worthy as your other sort done bad, a' b'lieve, souls; so say I.'

'Four breaths, and then the last,' said the leader authoritatively. '"Rejoice, ye Tenants of the Earth," number sixty-four.'

At the close, waiting yet another minute, he said in a clear loud voice, as he had said in the village at that hour and season for the previous forty years—

'A merry Christmas to ye!'

When the expectant stillness consequent upon the exclamation had nearly died out of them all, an increasing light made itself visible in one of the windows of the upper floor. It came so close to the blind that the exact position of the flame could be perceived from the outside. Remaining steady for an instant, the blind went upward from before it, revealing to thirty concentrated eyes a young girl, framed as a picture by the window architrave, and unconsciously illuminating her countenance to a vivid brightness by a candle she held in her left hand, close to her face, her right hand being extended to the side of the window. She was wrapped in a white robe of some kind, whilst down her shoulders fell a twining profusion of marvellously rich hair, in a wild disorder which proclaimed it to be only during the invisible hours of the night that such a condition was discoverable. Her bright eyes were looking into the grey world outside with an uncertain expression, oscillating between courage and shyness, which, as she recognised the semicircular group of dark forms gathered before her, transformed itself into pleasant resolution.

Opening the window, she said lightly and warmly – 'Thank you, singers, thank you!'

Together went the window quickly and quietly, and the blind started downward on its return to its place. Her fair forehead and eyes vanished; her little mouth; her neck and shoulders; all of her. Then the spot of candlelight shone nebulously as before; then it moved away.

'How pretty! exclaimed Dick Dewy.

'If she'd been rale wexwork she couldn't ha' been comelier,' said Michael Mail.

'Opening the window, she said lightly and warmly – "Thank you, singers, thank you!"' Marguerite Allan as Fancy Day in Harry Lachman's film of Under the Greenwood Tree, *made in about 1928.*

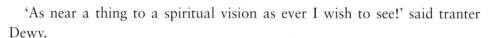

'As near a thing to a spiritual vision as ever I wish to see!' said tranter Dewy.

'O, sich I never, never see!' said Leaf fervently.

All the rest, after clearing their throats and adjusting their hats, agreed that such a sight was worth singing for.

'Now to Farmer Shiner's, and then replenish our insides, father?' said the tranter.

'Wi' all my heart,' said old William, shouldering his bass-viol.

Farmer Shiner's was a queer lump of a house, standing at the corner of a lane that ran into the principal thoroughfare. The upper windows were much wider than they were high, and this feature, together with a broad bay-window where the door might have been expected, gave it by day the aspect of a human countenance turned askance, and wearing a sly and wicked leer. To-night nothing was visible but the outline of the roof upon the sky.

The front of this building was reached, and the preliminaries arranged as usual.

'Four breaths, and number thirty-two, "Behold the Morning Star,"' said old William.

They had reached the end of the second verse, and the fiddlers were doing the up bow-stroke previously to pouring forth the opening chord of the third verse, when, without a light appearing or any signal being given, a roaring voice exclaimed—

'Shut up, woll 'ee! Don't make your blaring row here! A feller wi' a headache enough to split his skull likes a quiet night!'

Slam went the window.

'Hullo, that's a' ugly blow for we!' said the tranter, in a keenly appreciative voice, and turning to his companions.

'Finish the carrel, all who be friends of harmony!' commanded old William; and they continued to the end.

'Four breaths, and number nineteen!' said William firmly. 'Give it him well; the quire can't be insulted in this manner!'

A light now flashed into existence, the window opened, and the farmer stood revealed as one in a terrific passion.

'Drown en! – drown en!' the tranter cried, fiddling frantically. 'Play fortissimy, and drown his spaking!'

'Fortissimy!' said Michael Mail, and the music and singing waxed so loud that it was impossible to know what Mr Shiner had said, was saying, or was about to say; but wildly flinging his arms and body about in the forms of capital Xs and Ys, he appeared to utter enough invectives to consign the whole parish to perdition.

'Very onseemly – very!' said old William, as they retired. 'Never such a dreadful scene in the whole round o' my carrel practice – never! And he a churchwarden!'

'Only a drap o' drink got into his head,' said the tranter. 'Man's well enough when he's in his religious frame. He's in his worldly frame now. Must ask en to our bit of a party to-morrow night, I suppose, and so put en in humour again. We bear no mortal man ill-will.'

Eventually, after serenading the vicar, and a stop for refreshment, the members of the quire reach their beds, and a somewhat attenuated repose. But their Christmas duties are far from over.

It being Christmas-day, the tranter prepared himself with Sunday particularity. Loud sousing and snorting noises were heard to proceed from a tub in the back quarters of the dwelling, proclaiming that he was there performing his great Sunday wash, lasting half-an-hour, to which his washings on working-day mornings were mere flashes in the pan. Vanishing into the outhouse with a large brown towel, and the above-named bubblings and snortings being carried on for about twenty minutes, the tranter would appear round the edge of the door, smelling like a summer fog, and looking as if he had just narrowly escaped a watery grave with the loss of much of his clothes, having since been weeping bitterly till his eyes were red; a crystal drop of water hanging ornamentally at the bottom of each ear, one at the tip of his nose, and others in the form of spangles about his hair.

Ablutions completed, three generations of the Dewy family set off with their instruments.

At the foot of an incline the church became visible through the north gate, or 'church hatch,' as it was called here. Seven agile figures in a clump were observable beyond, which proved to be the choristers waiting; sitting on an altar-tomb to pass the time, and letting their heels dangle against it. The musicians being now in sight, the youthful party scampered off and rattled up the old wooden stairs of the gallery like a regiment of cavalry, the other boys of the parish waiting outside and observing birds, cats, and other creatures till the vicar entered, when they suddenly subsided into sober churchgoers, and passed down the aisle with echoing heels.

The gallery of Mellstock Church had a status and sentiment of its own. A stranger there was regarded with a feeling altogether differing from that of the congregation below towards him. Banished ftom the nave as an intruder whom no originality could make interesting, he was received above as a curiosity that no unfitness could render dull. The gallery, too, looked down upon and knew the habits of the nave to its remotest peculiarity, and had an

The Mellstock Quire in action, from the 1920s' film.

extensive stock of exclusive information about it; whilst the nave knew nothing of the gallery folk, as gallery folk, beyond their loud-sounding minims and chest notes. Such topics as that the clerk was always chewing tobacco except at the moment of crying amen; that he had a dust-hole in his pew; that during the sermon certain young daughters of the village had left off caring to read anything so mild as the marriage service for some years, and now regularly studied the one which chronologically follows it; that a pair of lovers touched fingers through a knot-hole between their pews in the manner ordained by their great exemplars, Pyramus and Thisbe; that Mrs Ledlow, the farmer's wife, counted her money and reckoned her week's marketing expenses during the first lesson – all news to those below – were stale subjects here.

Old William sat in the centre of the front row, his violoncello between his knees and two singers on each hand. Behind him, on the left, came the treble singers and Dick; and on the right the tranter and the tenors. Farther back was old Mail with the altos and supernumeraries . . .

The music on Christmas mornings was frequently below the standard of church-performances at other times. The boys were sleepy from the heavy exertions of the night; the men were slightly wearied, and now, in addition to these constant reasons, there was a dampness in the atmosphere that still further aggravated the evil. Their strings, from the recent long exposure to the night air, rose whole semitones, and snapped with a loud twang at the most silent moment; which necessitated more retiring than ever to the back of the gallery, and made the gallery throats quite husky with the quantity of coughing and hemming required for tuning in. The vicar looked cross.

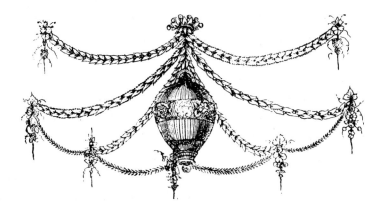

Crusted Characters

Thomas Hardy

The Mellstock Quire's days were numbered, but at least their exit from the gallery was not the result of any mistake as dramatic as that of their colleagues at 'Longpuddle' (probably Piddletrenthide, or possibly Puddletown, both villages close to Stinsford). Nor were any of their members detected as impostors trying to procure an undeserved supper. These misfortunes are the subject of two of Hardy's most light-hearted short stories, Old Andrey's Experience as a Musician, *and* Absent-Mindedness in a Parish Choir. *They are narrated in* A Few Crusted Characters, *which was published with* Life's Little Ironies *in 1894.*

Old Andrey's Experience as a Musician

'I was one of the quire-boys at that time, and we and the players were to appear at the manor-house as usual that Christmas week, to play and sing in the hall to the squire's people and visitors (among 'em being the archdeacon, Lord and Lady Baxby, and I don't know who); afterwards going, as we always did, to have a good supper in the servants' hall. Andrew knew this was the custom, and meeting us when we were starting to go, he said to us: "Lord, how I should like to join in that meal of beef, and turkey, and plum-pudding, and ale, that you happy ones be going to just now! One more or less will make no difference to the squire. I am too old to pass as a singing boy, and too bearded to pass as a singing girl; can ye lend me a fiddle, neighbours, that I may come with ye as a bandsman?"

'Well, we didn't like to be hard upon him, and lent him an old one, though Andrew knew no more of music than the Giant o' Cernel; and armed with the instrument he walked up to the squire's house with the others of us at the time appointed, and went in boldly, his fiddle under his arm. He made himself as natural as he could in opening the music-books and moving the candles to the best points for throwing light upon the notes; and all went well till we had played and sung "While shepherds watch," and "Star, arise," and "Hark the glad sound." Then the squire's mother, a tall gruff old lady, who was much interested in church-music, said quite unexpectedly to Andrew: "My man, I see you don't play your instrument with the rest. How is that?"

'Every one of the quire was ready to sink into the earth with concern at the fix Andrew was in. We could see that he had fallen into a cold sweat, and how he would get out of it we did not know.

'"I've had a misfortune, mem," he says, bowing as meek as a child. "Coming along the road I fell down and broke my bow."

'"O, I am sorry to hear that," says she. "Can't it be mended?"

'"O no, mem," says Andrew. "Twas broke all to splinters."

'"I'll see what I can do for you," says she.

'And then it seemed all over, and we played "Rejoice, ye drowsy mortals all," in D and two sharps. But no sooner had we got through it than she says to Andrew,

'"I've sent up into the attic, where we have some old musical instruments, and found a bow for you." And she hands the bow to poor wretched Andrew, who didn't even know which end to take hold of. "Now we shall have the full accompaniment," says she.

'Andrew's face looked as if it were made of rotten apple as he stood in the circle of players in front of his book; for if there was one person in the parish that everybody was afraid of, 'twas this hook-nosed old lady. However, by keeping a little behind the next man he managed to make pretence of beginning, sawing away with his bow without letting it touch the strings, so that it looked as if he were driving into the tune with heart and soul. 'Tis a question if he wouldn't have got through all right if one of the squire's visitors (no other than the archdeacon) hadn't noticed that he held the fiddle upside down, the nut under his chin, and the tail-piece in his hand; and they began to crowd round him, thinking 'twas some new way of performing.

'This revealed everything; the squire's mother had Andrew turned out of the house as a vile impostor, and there was great interruption to the harmony of the proceedings, the squire declaring he should have notice to leave his cottage that day fortnight. However, when we got to the servants' hall there sat Andrew, who had been let in at the back door by the orders of the squire's wife, after being turned out at the front by the orders of the squire, and nothing more was heard about his leaving his cottage. But Andrew never performed in public as a musician after that night; and now he's dead and gone, poor man, as we all shall be!

Hardy's drawing of the west gallery in Stinsford Church. After the musicians abandoned the gallery, it was demolished, and Hardy has drawn it from memory. However, it has recently been reconstructed as authentically as possible, and was consecrated at Christmas 1996.

Absent-Mindedness in a Parish Choir

'It happened on Sunday after Christmas – the last Sunday ever they played in Longpuddle church gallery, as it turned out, though they didn't know it then. As you may know, sir, the players formed a very good band – almost as good as the Mellstock parish players that were led by the Dewys; and that's saying a great deal. There was Nicholas Puddingcome, the leader, with the first fiddle; there was Timothy Thomas, the bass-viol man; John Biles, the tenor fiddler; Dan'l Hornhead, with the serpent; Robert Dowdle, with the clarionet; and Mr. Nicks, with the oboe – all sound and powerful musicians, and strong-winded men – they that blowed. For that reason they were very much in demand Christmas week for little reels and dancing

99

Puddletown's fine parish church has preserved its musicians' gallery.

parties; for they could turn a jig or a hornpipe out of hand as well as ever they could turn out a psalm, and perhaps better, not to speak irreverent. In short, one half-hour they could be playing a Christmas carol in the squire's hall to the ladies and gentlemen, and drinkin' tay and coffee with 'em as modest as saints; and the next, at The Tinker's Arms, blazing away like wild horses with the "Dashing White Sergeant" to nine couple of dancers and more, and swallowing rum-and-cider hot as flame.

'Well, this Christmas they'd been out to one rattling randy after another every night, and had got next to no sleep at all. Then came the Sunday after Christmas, their fatal day. 'Twas so mortal cold that year that they could hardly sit in the gallery; for though the congregation down in the body of the church had a stove to keep off the frost, the players in the gallery had nothing at all. So Nicholas said at morning service, when 'twas freezing an inch an hour, "Please the Lord I won't stand this numbing weather no longer: this afternoon we'll have something in our insides to make us warm, if it cost a king's ransom."

'So he brought a gallon of hot brandy and beer, ready mixed, to church with him in the afternoon, and by keeping the jar well wrapped up in Timothy Thomas's bass-viol bag it kept drinkably warm till they wanted it, which was just a thimbleful in the Absolution, and another after the Creed, and the remainder at the beginning o' the sermon. When they'd had the last pull they felt quite comfortable and warm, and as the sermon went on – most unfortunately for 'em it was a long one that afternoon – they fell asleep, every man jack of 'em; and there they slept on as sound as rocks.

''Twas a very dark afternoon, and by the end of the sermon all you could see of the inside of the church were the pa'son's two candles alongside of him in the pulpit, and his spaking face behind 'em. The sermon being ended at last, the pa'son gie'd out the Evening Hymn. But no quire set about sounding up the tune, and the people began to turn their heads to learn the reason why, and then Levi Limpet, a boy who sat in the gallery, nudged Timothy and Nicholas, and said, "Begin! begin!"

'"Hey? what?" says Nicholas, starting up; and the church being so dark and his head so muddled he thought he was at the party they had played at all the night before, and away he went, bow and fiddle, at "The Devil among the Tailors," the favourite jig of our neighbourhood at that time. The rest of the band, being in the same state of mind and nothing doubting, followed their leader with all their strength, according to custom. They poured out that there tune till the lower bass notes of "The Devil among the Tailors" made the

cobwebs in the roof shiver like ghosts; then Nicholas, seeing nobody moved, shouted out as he scraped (in his usual commanding way at dances when the folk didn't know the figures), "Top couples cross hands! And when I make the fiddle squeak at the end, every man kiss his pardner under the mistletoe!"

'The boy Levi was so frightened that he bolted down the gallery stairs and out homeward like lightning. The pa'son's hair fairly stood on end when he heard the evil tune raging through the church, and thinking the quire had gone crazy he held up his hand and said: "Stop, stop, stop! Stop, stop! What's this?" But they didn't hear'n for the noise of their own playing, and the more he called the louder they played.

'Then the folks came out of their pews, wondering down to the ground, and saying: "What do they mean by such wickedness! We shall be consumed like Sodom and Gomorrah!"

'And the squire, too, came out of his pew lined wi' green baize, where lots of lords and ladies visiting at the house were worshipping along with him, and went and stood in front of the gallery, and shook his fist in the musicians' faces, saying, "What! In this reverent edifice! What!"

'And at last they heard'n through their playing, and stopped.

'"Never such an insulting, disgraceful thing – never!" says the squire, who couldn't rule his passion.

'"Never!" says the pa'son, who had come down and stood beside him.

'"Not if the Angels of Heaven," says the squire (he was a wickedish man, the squire was, though now for once he happened to be on the Lord's side), – 'not if the Angels of Heaven come down," he says, "shall one of you villainous players ever sound a note in this church again; for the insult to me, and my family, and my visitors, and the parson, and God Almighty, that you've a-perpetrated this afternoon!"

'Then the unfortunate church band came to their senses, and remembered where they were; and 'twas a sight to see Nicholas Puddingcome and Timothy Thomas and John Biles creep down the gallery stairs with their fiddles under their arms, and poor Dan'l Hornhead with his serpent, and Robert Dowdle with his clarionet, all looking as little as ninepins; and out they went. The pa'son might have forgi'ed 'em when he learned the truth o't, but the squire would not. That very week he sent for a barrel-organ that would play two-and-twenty new psalm-tunes, so exact and particular that, however sinful inclined you was, you could play nothing but psalm-tunes whatsomever. He had a really respectable man to turn the winch, as I said, and the old players played no more.'

By 1900 the popularity of Hardy's novels had prompted literary pilgrims to seek out the Wessex locations, and a string of guidebooks followed. The fine illustrator, E.H. New, drew Weatherbury (Puddletown) Church, showing its west gallery, for a 1902 publication, The Wessex of Thomas Hardy.

The Paphian Ball

Thomas Hardy

*The Mellstock Quire, in fact, according to one of Hardy's most
intriguing supernatural poems, had made precisely the opposite mistake.*

We went our Christmas rounds once more,
With quire and viols as theretofore.

Our path was near by Rushy-Pond,
Where Egdon-Heath outstretched beyond.

There stood a figure against the moon,
Tall, spare, and humming a weirdsome tune.

'You tire of Christian carols, he said:
'Come and lute at a ball instead.

''Tis to your gain, for it ensures
That many guineas will be yours.

'A slight condition hangs on't, true,
But you will scarce say nay thereto:

'That you go blindfold; that anon
The place may not be gossiped on.'

They stood and argued with each other:
'Why sing from one house to another

'These ancient hymns in the freezing night,
And all for nought? 'Tis foolish, quite!'

'—'Tis serving God, and shunning evil:
Might not elsedoing serve the devil?'

'But grand pay!' . . . They were lured by his call,
Agreeing to go blindfold all.

They walked, he guiding, some new track,
Doubting to find the pathway back.

In a strange hall they found them when
They were unblinded all again.

Gilded alcoves, great chandeliers,
Voluptuous paintings ranged in tiers,

In brief, a mansion large and rare,
With rows of dancers waiting there.

They tuned and played; the couples danced;
Half-naked women tripped, advanced,

With handsome partners footing fast,
Who swore strange oaths, and whirled them past.

And thus and thus the slow hours wore them:
While shone their guineas heaped before them.

Drowsy at length, in lieu of the dance
'While Shepherds watched . . .' they bowed by chance;

And in a moment, at a blink,
There flashed a change; ere they could think

The ball-room vanished and all its crew:
Only the well-known heath they view—

The spot of their crossing overnight,
When wheedled by the stranger's sleight.

*Rainbarrow, 'bulged like a supine negress' breast'. E.H. New's drawing for the
1902 guidebook.*

There, east, the Christmas dawn hung red,
And dark Rainbarrow with its dead

Bulged like a supine negress' breast
Against Clyffe-Clump's faint far-off crest.

Yea; the rare mansion, gorgeous, bright,
The ladies, gallants, gone were quite.

The heaped-up guineas, too, were gone
With the gold table they were on.

'Why did not grasp we what was owed!'
Cried some, as homeward, shamed, they strode.

Now comes the marvel and the warning:
When they had dragged to church next morning,

With downcast heads and scarce a word,
They were astound at what they heard.

Hardy's first volume of poetry, Wessex Poems, *published in 1898, included numerous drawings by Hardy himself. This is the melody of a popular dance tune, 'Soldier's Joy', drawn to illustrate a Christmas poem, 'The Dance at the Phoenix'.*

Praises from all came forth in showers
For how they'd cheered the midnight hours.

'We've heard you many times, friends said,
'But like that never have you played!

'*Rejoice, ye tenants of the earth,*
And celebrate your Saviour's birth,

'Never so thrilled the darkness through,
Or more inspired us so to do!' . . .

—The man who used to tell this tale
Was the tenor-viol, Michael Mail;

Yes; Mail the tenor, now but earth!—
I give it for what it may be worth.

Christmas in the Elgin Room

Thomas Hardy

Paphos, from which that poem, 'The Paphian Ball', takes its name, was
an ancient Greek city on the island of Cyprus, famous for its temple to
Venus. Its inhabitants were reputed to have shared their goddess's
tendencies. And so, by transferring the epithet to legendary Dorset,
Hardy combined his interests in classical civilization, local folklore and
customs, and the interplay between Christianity and pagan superstition.
The last poem published during his lifetime was devoted to precisely
the same conflict. He seems to have formulated the idea for 'Christmas
in the Elgin Room' while researching material for The Dynasts *in the*
British Museum in 1905. Perhaps significantly, this was probably the

*year when he first met Florence Dugdale, who was to become his second
wife, and who at the beginning of their relationship helped him by
following up references in the Reading Room. The poem (subtitled
'British Museum: early last century') was completed in 1926 and
submitted to* The Times *for publication on Christmas Eve 1927. By then
Hardy was dying, but was pleased when a warm appreciation of the
piece arrived from the editor of* The Times, *and another from an old
friend, Sir Edmund Gosse. His reply to Gosse, written on Christmas
Day, was the last letter he wrote.*

'What is the noise that shakes the night,
And seems to soar to the Pole-star height?'
—'Christmas bells,
The watchman tells
Who walks this hall that blears us captives with its blight.'

'And what, then, mean such clangs, so clear?'
'—'Tis said to have been a day of cheer,
And source of grace
To the human race
Long ere their woven sails winged us to exile here.

'We are those whom Christmas overthrew
Some centuries after Pheidias knew
How to shape us
And bedrape us
And to set us in Athena's temple for men's view.

'O it is sad now we are sold—
We gods! for Borean people's gold,
And brought to the gloom
Of this gaunt room
Which sunlight shuns, and sweet Aurore but enters cold.

'For all these bells, would I were still
Radiant as on Athenai's Hill.'
—'And I, and I!'

The others sigh,
'Before this Christ was known, and we had men's good will.'

Thereat old Helios could but nod,
Throbbed, too, the Ilissus River-god,
And the torsos there
Of deities fair,
Whose limbs were shards beneath some Acropolitan clod:

Demeter too, Poseidon hoar,
Persephone, and many more
Of Zeus' high breed,—
All loth to heed
What the bells sang that night which shook them to the core.

A Green Christmas

When he was interviewed for an American magazine, The Critic, *in 1901, the conversation turned on Hardy's interest in the supernatural.*

TH: . . . I am most anxious to believe in what, roughly speaking, we may call the supernatural – but I find no evidence for it! People accuse me of scepticism, materialism, and so forth; but, if the accusation is just at all, it is quite against my will. For instance, I seriously assure you that I would give ten years of my life – well, perhaps that offer is rather beyond my means – but when I was a younger man, I would cheerfully have given ten years of my life to see a ghost – an authentic, indubitable spectre.

Interviewer: And you have never seen one?

TH: Never the ghost of a ghost. Yet I should think I am cut out by nature for a ghost-seer. My nerves vibrate very readily; people say I am almost morbidly imaginative; my will to believe is

perfect. If ever ghost wanted to manifest itself, I am the very man he should apply to. But no – the spirits don't seem to see it!

Interviewer: Yet you live in a graveyard, too, don't you?

TH: A Roman graveyard – yes. We decapitated a row of five Roman soldiers or colonists in moving the earth to make the drive there.

Interviewer: And wasn't there a lady as well?

TH: Yes. I think I showed you the little bronze-gilt fibula that had fastened the fillet across her brow. I took it from her skull with my own hands, and it lies in the corner cupboard yonder.

Interviewer: Yet she hasn't haunted you? Well, that certainly establishes a very strong presumption against the spooks . . .

But that was not the last word. On Christmas Eve 1919, when he no longer had ten years of his life left to give, Hardy did see a ghost. His wife reported the fact, tagged to a more mundane domestic upset, in a letter written three days later.

We had a very quiet Christmas, we too, alone, with Wessie [their notorious dog, Wessex] – our only diversion being that TH *would* give Wessie goose and plum-pudding, and the result was what might have been expected – and he (TH) didn't even clean up the result, as he ought. He saw a ghost in Stinsford Churchyard on Christmas Eve, and his sister Kate says it must have been their grandfather upon whose grave TH had just placed a sprig of holly – the first time he had ever done so. The ghost said: 'A green Christmas' – TH replied 'I like a green Christmas'. Then the ghost went into the church, and being full of curiosity, T followed, to see who this strange man in 18th century dress might be – and found – no-one. That is quite true – a real Christmas ghost story.

This exchange between Hardy and the ghost of the grandfather whom he had never known, but whose portrait he had so lovingly painted as one of the Mellstock Quire, is remarkable in itself, but when the underlying folklore is considered their remarks are invested with added irony. Here is John Symons Udal on the subject of unseasonable weather at Christmas:

As a West Country variant of the common saying that 'A green Christmas makes a fat churchyard', Mr Norris gives the following as indicating the

The grave of Hardy's grandfather, also Thomas Hardy, in Stinsford Church. It was here, on Christmas Eve 1919, that his ghost appeared to Hardy.

fatal effects of a trying spring on the constitutions of the sick and aged who have survived a mild winter: 'Ev a chich'ard da look lik' a pastur' veel 'pon C'ursmas Day 'll look lik' a plow'd veel avoa Medzumma Day.'

Hardy, set to celebrate his eightieth birthday between that ghostly Christmas encounter and the following midsummer, might with some justification have felt forebodings, and became decidedly touchy when accused of pessimism in that February's issue of a literary magazine. On the other hand, he might have taken comfort from his grandfather's self-confessed capacity for diabolical practical joking. Hardy himself supplied this story, which was included by a lecturer on dew-ponds at a meeting of the Dorset Natural History and Antiquarian Society in 1912.

By the courtesy of Mr Thomas Hardy I am permitted to give you, in his own words, an account of the following interesting adventure which happened to an ancestor of his (the author's grandfather), beside this very pond [Greenhill Pond, on Puddletown Heath], as nearly as possible a century ago. He was crossing the heath, one midnight in June, by the path which then, as now, skirts the pond, when he became aware that he was followed by two men whom he had noticed watching him when he left Puddletown. He had now little doubt that they were bent on attacking and robbing him, for times were more lawless then than they are at present. It had so happened that while crossing a green field called Coomb a little earlier in his journey, he had been struck by the great number of glow-worms that were shining in the grass, and being a young man he beguiled his walk by gathering several and placing them on the brim of his hat. As he was unarmed, and the men were gaining upon him, the only way of escape that occurred to him was by playing upon their superstitious feelings. He accordingly rolled a furze faggot into the path, and, sitting down upon it, took off his hat, placed it on his knees, stuck two fir fronds on his head to represent horns, and pulled from his pocket a letter he chanced to have with him, and began reading it by the light of the glow-worms. The men approached, stopped suddenly, and then bolted at the top of their speed down the hill and disappeared. In a few days there was a rumour in the neighbourhood that the devil had been seen at midnight by Greenhill Pond, reading a list of his victims by glow-worm light. He tried afterwards to discover who the men were, but they never revealed their identity.

A Girt Big House-Dog

William Barnes

*Hardy had set a ghost story at Christmas many years before seeing one
for real, in his poem 'The Dead Quire' which ends this selection. So too
had William Barnes, in his poem, 'Eclogue: a Ghost'. His was not the
ghost of a person, but of a large dog – another commonplace of folklore.*

> . . . Aye; did ye ever hear – vo'k zaid 'twer true—
> O' what bevell Jack Hine zome years agoo?
> Woone vrosty night, d'ye know, at Chris'mas tide,
> Jack, an' another chap or two bezide,
> 'D a-been out, zomewhere up at tother end
> O' parish, to a naighbour's house to spend
> A merry hour, an' mid a-took a cup
> Or two o' eale a-keepen Chris'mas up;
> Zoo I do lot 'twer leate avore the pearty
> 'D a-burnt their bron out; I do lot, avore
> They thought o' turnen out o' door
> 'Twer mornen, vor their friendship then wer hearty.
> Well; clwose agean the vootpath that do lead
> Vrom higher parish over withy-mead,
> There's still a hollow, you do know: they tried there,
> In former times, to meake a cattle-pit,
> But gi'ed it up, because they coulden get
> The water any time to bide there.
> Zoo when the merry fellows got
> Just overright thease lwonesome spot,
> Jack zeed a girt big house-dog wi' a collar,
> A-stannen down in thik there hollor.
> Lo'k there, he zaid, there's zome girt dog a-prowlen:
> I'll just goo down an' gi'en a goodish lick
> Or two wi' thease here groun'-ash stick,
> An' zend the shaggy rascal hwome a-howlen.

Zoo there he run, an' gi'ed en a good whack
Wi' his girt ashen stick athirt his back;
An', all at woonce, his stick split right all down
In vower pieces; an' the pieces vled
Out ov his hand all up above his head,
An' pitch'd in vower corners o' the groun'.
An' then he velt his han' get all so num',
He coulden veel a vinger or a thum';
An' after that his earm begun to zwell,
An' in the night a-bed he vound
The skin o't peelen off all round.
'Twer near a month avore he got it well.

Winter Poems

William Barnes

*It is wintry weather, rather than a green Christmas, that we expect from
a poet at this time of year. Although the majority of his output was
written in Dorset dialect, Barnes also wrote poetry in standard English,
and here are two commendable examples evoking the harshness of
winter in the countryside.*

The Holly Tree

Green holly, glittering in the gleams
Of gloomy winter, when the beams
Of western suns break wan between
The wat'ry clouds, and winds blow keen
Through leafless hawthorns, growing high
In hedge below thy chilly sky;
Thy life betokens, as we tread
The trackless beds of leaves all dead,

That though, in wint'ry winds, they now
Have wither'd on their shaken bough,
The shrouds that shed them at our feet
Will share again the quick'ning heat
Of lofty suns, and groves shall grow
All green again in summer's glow.
O holly green, unheeded child
Of heathy slope, and woodland wild,
Of evergreens with limbs bent low
By loads of lightly-sinking snow,
But few are left, O lonely tree,
With less of heed or help than thee.
The clinging ivy-stem, that cleaves
To cloud-high trees, with glist'ning leaves,
Or with its crooked limbs o'ercrawls
The crevices of lofty walls,
Holds steady by its trusty stay
When storms begloom the winter's day.
The mistletoe, disowning earth,
The air-fed child of lofty birth,
Keeps on her sunny tree her seat
Unsoil'd by touch of earth-borne feet;
While o'er the grey old headstone grows
The green-bark'd yew, wall'd in from foes
In hallow'd ground, to hang its head
Unharm'd, o'ershadowing the dead.
The forest fir that seems to mock
Its foes upon the ragged rock,
With twisting roots holds firmly fast
By faithful cliffs, and bears the blast;
And weatherbeaten walls inclose
The winter laurel from its foes,
Where, near the house, its scanty screen
Beskirts the walk upon the green;
And some fair girl, who first has felt
Her fulfraught heart with true love melt,
When fields are wearing, wide below

Her window, glitt'ring coats of snow,
Steals meekly from her mother's eyes,
To meditate by twilight skies;
And walks, unoccupied by aught
But one dear name, in blissful thought
Of bridal days still breaking blest
To bring her joy and leave her rest.
But no strong fence nor faithful tree
Affords a saving strength to thee,
Green holly, standing on thy hill
Unheeded, but preserv'd from ill
By thorn-sharp prickles thrilling keen
A threat'ning foe, fair evergreen;
Thus showing, holy shrub, the low
Unshielded souls o'erwhelm'd with woe,
That God in love will never leave
O'erlook'd his children when they grieve.
When winter brings the welcome morn
That warns us of a Saviour born,
And meeting kindred bring to mind
The mercy God has shown our kind,
Thy ruddy berries, set around
The room, are shaken by the sound
Of festive laugh, and freaky joke,
Of frolic-loving younger folk,
While mothers, smiling side by side,
All see their daughters' mirth with pride,
Enjoying o'er, in melting mood,
Their mirthful games of maidenhood,
Forgetful of the time to go
Through gath'ring sheets of glitt'ring snow;
Till low Orion faintly lights
Their lonely road, from western heights.
So live undying to adorn
Our day of joy thou tree forlorn;
Still meeting mirth and hearty cheer,
And music welcoming the year,

In happy homes where love may glow
In hearts but little tried with woe.

A Winter Night

It was a chilly winter's night;
And frost was glitt'ring on the ground,
And evening stars were twinkling bright;
And from the gloomy plain around
Came no sound,
But where, within the wood-girt tow'r,
The churchbell slowly struck the hour;

As if that all of human birth
Had risen to the final day,
And soaring from the wornout earth
Were called in hurry and dismay,
Far away;
And I alone of all mankind
Were left in loneliness behind.

A Winter scene. Wood engraving by Clare Leighton for the 1940 illustrated edition of Under the Greenwood Tree.

Winter Night in the Country

Ralph Wightman

The little strip of Dorset countryside east of Dorchester, which extends from the valley of the Piddle to the valley of the Frome, was described in all its moods by William Barnes (1801–86) and Thomas Hardy (1840–1928). In his way, Ralph Wightman (1901–71) carried on the tradition as a broadcaster and writer. He was born at Piddletrenthide and made his home at Puddletown, on the edge of Hardy's Egdon Heath. Here is his description of the winter countryside, published twenty years after Hardy's death.

Before the War townsmen used to go out in the evening much oftener and stay out much later than countrymen. Yet as long as they remained in the great cities they were never out at night, because night was turned into an artificial day for them. There must have been thousands of children in London who had never seen the stars before 1939.

To me it is a terrible thought that human beings should be able to grow up with no conception of the beauty and mystery of night. I do not think it is possible to feel it in any town, perhaps not even in a village. Now that the blackout restrictions have been lifted the village street is much as it always was. There never were any street lamps, but there were several friendly patches of light from the windows of our neighbours. To experience the grandeur of the night it is necessary to get away from the houses up to the bare hills. A still frosty night in November with no moon is the best time of all. You do not need any of the learning of the modern Wise Men about the planets and light years to appreciate the immensity of space. The modern truth that each of those living lights is a world seems an old fable. The story of the Ancient Wise Men and their Star is easier to believe.

I suppose to a townsman the first impression of night on the hills is of silence. He can hear his own breathing, he wants to whistle or sing for company. Perhaps it isn't so much the silence as the sounds which he might hear if he didn't keep moving and make a brave noise. If you stand very still on the hills at night you will hear many strange rustlings and creakings. As soon as you move they will cease but a minute of silence will start them off again. Man, domestic animals, and most of the birds work in daylight and sleep when darkness falls. The wild creatures of the hedges do their business at night. If you flash a torch on a patch of fertile soil you will surprise dozens of worms in their labour of dragging dead leaves down into the earth. You will catch the slugs at their work of destruction. You may see little pin points of light where a field mouse has frozen into stillness with only its eyes alive. The field mouse is not likely to be out at this time of the year unless the weather is very mild, he is wise enough to sleep through most of the English winter.

The badger is still about, although he will spend weeks in his earth if it snows. You can hear him coming from a quarter of a mile away on a still night. He has no natural enemies and is never at all concerned to move quietly. He crashes through the undergrowth like a pig and grunts like a pig as he does it. Another sound you might hear on the hills at night is the complaining of a hedgehog. You have probably all seen this English porcupine rolled up in a ball the size of a coconut with all his prickles erect, but perhaps you have never heard him. He always seems to be in tearful mood, and moves along snuffling and wheezing like a very bad tempered dwarf with a cold. He hibernates most of the winter and it is a bit late to find him now.

The rabbits do most of their feeding in the late evening and early morning. Sooner or later you will be sure to hear that almost human scream of a rabbit at the point of death. They make no vocal noise in their lives until that last second when the jaws of a trap have closed, or they feel the teeth of a stoat or fox. Then they scream horribly, and I think that cry is the reason for a great deal of the sentiment which people feel for rabbits. In addition of course they do look charming. A young rabbit washing his face looks most appealing and helpless. All the baby books of our childhood contained pictures of rabbits mixed up with toadstools and fairies. Well, I don't know about fairies, but toadstools can be poisonous, and rabbits are nothing but vermin. I have worked out some figures which I believe are reasonably accurate, although too boring to give you now, which show that every rabbit I catch on my farm has done at least one pound's worth of damage to human food. When I have caught him he is worth as food about one tenth of that amount. I hate to hear that scream in the night, but I steel my heart and think 'good, that is one less rabbit in the wheat'.

Perhaps the most blood curdling sound of the countryside at night is the cry of an owl. The flight of an owl is absolutely silent. With all other birds you can hear the beat of the wings, and the swish of their passage through the air. An owl moves as silently as a ghost. He floats along the line of a hedge, and every now and then he gives that unnatural blood freezing cry. I remember once that I was leaning on a gate waiting for Shepherd and an owl came to investigate me. He hovered just over my head with his great wings motionless and his huge eyes mesmerising me. It took a real effort of will to make a movement and scare him away. For a moment I could easily have been really frightened. Generally speaking owls are the friends of the farmer. They eat enormous numbers of mice and rats, and the damage they do to young pheasants and partridges is more important in peace than in war.

A night sound which the townsman might not recognise at first is the barking of a fox. This is absolutely different from that of a dog, and if he listens he will soon have both noises for comparison. I am sure that the fox barks on occasion with the malicious purpose of taunting the dogs tied up in the village. There is one old dog fox who prowls round the hen houses in the orchard at night and drives my sheepdog into an absolute frenzy. One of these nights with a moon if I can only restrain my desire for a smoke, I shall get him with a shot gun. Talking of smoking, have you ever noticed how scents persist in the air at night? The heap of manure in the corner of barn field is unnoticeable all day but I have caught a whiff of it across half a mile at night. The breath of the cows hang on the evening air. It is sweet and heavy, a fragrance of clover and rich content. It is a rather alarming experience to fall over a sleeping cow in the dark.

I like the sheepfold at night. It gives me a feeling of having a place in one of the oldest and most honourable occupations of men. The same cold stars have looked down for so many thousand years on sheep safely folded for the night. When my neighbour has his last look round in the evening he carries a light which is the exact pattern of the lanterns which have been in use for hundreds of years. The illumination is provided by a candle and the sides of the lantern are not made of glass but of thin sheets of horn. The light it gives is absolutely useless at a distance of two feet, but he insists that anything brighter would frighten the sheep. Perhaps my sheep are better educated. I have never found them the least bit frightened of the most powerful electric torch I could obtain. Still I am probably just as unreasonable about some other bit of tradition.

There will probably be a certain amount of activity on the hills at night which you will neither see nor hear. Almost every English village possesses one citizen who elects to work very hard at night, in considerable discomfort, and some danger from the law. The village poacher is seldom a bad character. He is not a thief in the sense that the town poacher is a thief. He likes to pit his wits against the game-keeper and the village constable. He works alone and has no facilities for the wholesale taking or disposal of game. Poaching is a hobby for him, not a living, although he expects his hobby to keep him in beer and tobacco. He enjoys his reputation at the village inn of being daring and crafty. The whole lining of his coat is one vast pocket and he can stow a hare and a brace of birds on his person without the suspicion of a bulge. As you walk down the lane from the hill there may be an extra dark shadow at one point in the hedge. Well, keep your torch on the road it is no business of yours. There will be no movement until your footsteps have died away.

Even on a moonless night there is more light on the hill than in the valley. The wood smoke from the cottages and the faint mist from the stream give a vapour which is almost invisible but which is still enough to dim the clearness of the stars. Even the leafless trees seem to absorb some of the faint light, and the evergreens in the church yard are completely black. Light is streaming out again, though, from the church windows – purple light and red and gold from the old stained glass. This is choir practice night, and if you stop to listen you will hear them having trouble with that tricky bit in the psalms. There is light too from the open door of the inn, light from the smithy, light from the chapel hall, light from the bakehouse, light from Joe Hunt's cowstall, light from every cottage. The road between may be dark but there are plenty of friendly lights as beacons. We do not need a blaze of illuminations to show us our familiar bit of the King's highway. Jock Pearson at the pub does not need a revolving sign to entice us to drink his beer. Every light in the country means something. Every light is friendly and useful. None of them puts out the stars.

Birds at Winter Nightfall

Thomas Hardy

Hardy's response to severe winter weather was compassion for the
animals and birds who had to fight to survive it. Both he and his first
wife, Emma, staunchly championed causes promoting animal welfare,
and found the shooting of gamebirds sickening. In a letter at Christmas
1905 he commented caustically about the seasonable habit of, 'killing a
host of harmless animals to eat gluttonously of, . . . by way of upholding
the truths of Christianity'. And his moving self-obituary, the poem
'Afterwards', includes the lines: 'When the hedgehog travels furtively
over the lawn, One may say, "He strove that such innocent creatures
should come to no harm . . ."'.
Snowfall turned his mind to the plight of birds.

Around the house the flakes fly faster,
And all the berries now are gone
From holly and cotonea-aster
Around the house. The flakes fly! – faster
Shutting indoors that crumb-outcaster
We used to see upon the lawn
Around the house. The flakes fly faster,
And all the berries now are gone!

BIRDS AT WINTER NIGHTFALL.
(*Triolet.*)

By THOMAS HARDY.

Around the house the flakes fly faster,
And all the berries now are gone
From holly and cotoneaster
Around the house. The flakes fly !—faster
Shutting indoors that crumb-outcaster
We used to see upon the lawn
Around the house. The flakes fly faster,
And all the berries now are gone !

   Max Gate.

All Good Wishes for Christmas and the New Year
from
Mr. and Mrs. Thomas Hardy.

A Christmas card incorporating a winter poem, sent by the Hardys, and now in Dorset
County Museum.

The Reminder

Thomas Hardy

The stark contrast between the cheery world indoors, and the suffering outside the window, pricked his conscience.

While I watch the Christmas blaze
Paint the room with ruddy rays,
Something makes my vision glide
To the frosty scene outside.

There, to reach a rotting berry,
Toils a thrush, – constrained to very
Dregs of food by sharp distress,
Taking such with thankfulness.

Why, O starving bird, when I
One day's joy would justify,
And put misery out of view,
Do you make me notice you!

A Glorious Bird

W.H. Hudson

During the final year of the nineteenth century – 1900, not 1899 – the naturalist W.H. Hudson published Nature in Downland, *which is still admired as one of his most successful country books. In it he described with typical enthusiasm the life-cycle of the missel-thrush.*

There is one thing to make a lover of bird-music happy in the darkest weather in January in this maritime district. Mid-winter is the season of the missel-thrush. The song-thrush has been heard since the end of November, but he is not the true winter singer. He is heard often enough – a bird here and a bird there – when the sun shines, and in cloudy or in wet weather too, if it be mild. But when it is too gloomy for even his fine temper, when there is no gleam of light anywhere and no change in that darkness of immense ever-moving cloud above; and the south-west raves all day and all night, and day after day, then the storm-cock sings his loudest from a tree-top and has no rival. A glorious bird!

He breeds earlier than most birds, and we have seen that after that labour is ended he repairs to the downs and leads a gipsy existence in bands of a dozen or so, feeding on snails and grasshoppers, drinking at the dew ponds, and resting at noon in the shade of the furze-bushes; also that in autumn he feasts (often too well) on wild fruits, especially the poisonous yew-berry. But during all that pleasant vagrant summer life, when he sings not and has no family cares, he is still in disposition the bird we know so well in the orchard and copse, the big olive-coloured spotty thrush that sits motionless and statuesque and flies from you with an angry scream; the bird whose courageous spirit and fierce onslaught in defence of his nest makes him the equal of crafty crows and pies, and of hawks, in spite of their hooked beaks and cruel sharp talons. Those large black conspicuous spots of his breast and his habit of singing in weather that makes all other voices silent, seem appropriate to a bird of his bold aggressive temper.

As I walked one hot day on the northern ridge of the South Downs, a party of half-a-dozen missel-thrushes flew up from the ground before me, and rising high in the air went away towards the weald. A telegraph line crosses the hills at that point, and just when the thrushes rose up and flew from me a sparrow-hawk came up swiftly flying over the ridge and perched on the telegraph wire. I have observed that this hawk, like the cuckoo, cannot properly grasp the wire and sit firm and upright on it as most passerine birds are able to do. Like the cuckoo he wobbles and drops his wings upon the wire to help to keep him up. It was so in the present case: the hawk was swaying about trying to hold on to the thin smooth wire when the thrushes passed over him, thirty or forty yards above, all but one, and this one remained hovering motionless in the air for a space of a few seconds directly above the hawk, then dropped like a stone upon his back, and knocked him clean off his perch.

It is often stated by writers on British birds that the missel-thrush ceases singing in March or April; this is a mistake, as I frequently hear him in May and June. But why, I have often asked myself, is he silent on many days in January and February when the weather is mild, and the song-thrush is loudest? I have a suspicion that the missel-thrush is less tolerant of other bird-voices near him than most species; and I think that the loud persistent singing of the song-thrush is more disturbing to him than any other bird-voice. At all events, I have often listened for the missel-thrush, in localities where he was abundant, and have not heard him when the song-thrush was singing. In the same localities I have heard the missel-thrush singing everywhere on days when his rival was silent.

When all the most luscious of the wild fruits have been eaten, and frosts and winds make the open downs impossible to live on, the missel-thrushes break up their flocks and every bird goes back to his lowland home. There is then not an orchard, nor copse, nor grove, without a pair of the big thrushes; and on the flat-wooded country on the north of the downs these birds are, I think, just as numerous. Home again from his long outing, the missel-thrush soon begins to sing; and if you should observe him in rough or gloomy weather, perched on an elm-top, swayed about this way and that by the gusts, singing his best, you must believe that this dark aspect of things delights him; that his pleasure in life, expressed with such sounds and in such circumstances, must greatly exceed in degree the contentment and bliss that is ours, even when we are most free from pain or care, and our whole beings most perfectly in tune with nature.

As to the song; although we probably value it most for its associations, and because it is often heard when other bird-voices are silent, it is also beautiful in itself. The sound is beautiful in quality, but the singer has no art, and flings out his notes anyhow; the song is an outburst, a cry of happiness, and is over in a moment, and after a moment of silence he repeats it, and so on for ten or twenty minutes or longer. In its quality the sound is most like the blackbird's; and when, in early spring, the blackbird, perched on a tree-top, first tries his long disused voice, the short confused phrases he blurts out are so like the song of the missel-thrush that any one may be easily deceived by them. The difference in the voices of the two birds is that the missel-thrush is not so full and mellow, and is slightly metallic or bell-like; and it is probably due to this quality that the song carries much further than that of the blackbird.

The Darkling Thrush

Thomas Hardy

It is Hudson's power of meticulous observation, allied to his total empathy with the creature he describes, which distinguishes his work. If Hardy had discovered this passage when it first appeared in print – as surely he must – he would have been struck by those words: 'you must believe that this dark aspect of things delights him'. It was precisely the image which he took up for his famous poem about the turn of the century.

The Missel Thrush by Thomas Bewick, from A History of British Birds, *vol. 1, 1826.*

'The Darkling Thrush' bears the date 31 December 1900, and we are intended to read it as if written at the last nightfall of the century. In fact it had been published in a magazine two days' earlier, and was originally entitled, 'By the Century's Deathbed'. The new title was skilfully chosen, as commentators have observed, since the unusual word 'darkling' had been used twice before in poems about birdsong: by Milton in Paradise Lost, *and by Keats in* Ode to a Nightingale. *More significantly, Matthew Arnold referred to the upheaval of belief which the nineteenth century had brought, as 'a darkling plain', in his influential poem 'Dover Beach', published in 1867. For Hardy the onset of the new century signified his maturity towards an uncertain old age (he celebrated his sixtieth birthday in 1900), the reluctant jettisoning of religious belief, and a distressingly faltering marriage. And yet, and yet – the missel-thrush delights in the dark aspect of things.*

I leant upon a coppice gate
When Frost was spectre-gray,
And Winter's dregs made desolate
The weakening eye of day.
The tangled bine-stems scored the sky
Like strings of broken lyres,
And all mankind that haunted nigh
Had sought their household fires.

The land's sharp features seemed to be
The Century's corpse outleant,
His crypt the cloudy canopy,
The wind his death-lament.
The ancient pulse of germ and birth
Was shrunken hard and dry,
And every spirit upon earth
Seemed fervourless as I.

At once a voice arose among
The bleak twigs overhead
In a full-hearted evensong
Of joy illimited;

An aged thrush, frail, gaunt, and small,
In blast-beruffled plume,
Had chosen thus to fling his soul
Upon the growing gloom.

So little cause for carolings
Of such ecstatic sound
Was written on terrestrial things
Afar or nigh around,
That I could think there trembled through
His happy good-night air
Some blessed Hope, whereof he knew
And I was unaware.

A Fine Moonlight Evening

The last day of the century, for which 'The Darkling Thrush' was written, spurred writers of every rank to attempt excellence. The reporter for the Dorset County Chronicle, Hardy's local newspaper, clearly took enormous pains to report the night's events at Dorchester in what he considered an appropriate way. He even invoked poetry (Cowper, not Hardy, alas!).

Exit the Nineteenth Century – Enter the Twentieth

The solemnity always associated with the close of a year was this year intensified – possibly ought to have been intensified a hundredfold – by the fact that the end of 1900 was also the end of the Nineteenth Century. With the vigil of watchnight services, with the requiem of muffled bell-peals, and also with the revelry of a wake, the old century was ushered to its rest, to be numbered with that ever-growing portion of eternity which we call the past. It departed laden with all the multitudinous joys and sorrows, hopes and fears, laughter and tears, successes and failures, of the most eventful and epoch-making hundred years of the whole world's history. Much matter did its departure afford for reflection to the contemplative mind; and in Dorchester, as in every other town throughout the land, special aids were offered to reflection, such as services at the churches and that throbbing bell-music which so stirs mind and heart and intensifies feeling.

> 'With easy force it opens all the cells
> Where memory sleeps.'

But men differ from one another in few things more than in the attitude they assume at such times. Silence and solemnity with some find their counterpart in riot and revelry with others. Possibly this phenomenon is of the necessity of things, and illustrates that rebound, that back-swing of the pendulum, which finds philosophic expression in the axiom, 'every action has its reaction'.

But the province of the news paragraphist is to chronicle events, not to soliloquise on abstruse speculations. At all the churches of the town but St Peter's, where a watchnight service was held, special services began at the reasonable hour of eight o'clock, when the streets were as yet quiet, and the congregations coming out of church had not to thread their way through a crowd of midnight wassailers. The services generally took the form of thanksgiving for the past and supplication for the future, and earnest, thought-stimulating addresses were delivered by the respective incumbents.

It was a fine moonlight evening, exceptionally exhilarating in such a season as we have been having. The wild tearing winds of the day had sunk to rest, leaving the roads dry and smooth and the air crisp; yet there was an aqueous aureole around the moon promising – or portending – more rain. This came to pass in the early morning. But on such a night it was a pleasure to be out of doors, and the promenaders and churchgoers were more than usually numerous. Muffled peals and changes were rung at intervals on the bells, both of St Peter's Church and of Fordington St George, and the Volunteer Band, under Bandmaster J. Stevens, played in the streets. Shortly before eleven the lights shining in St Peter's Church reminded the passers-by of the watchnight service about to begin . . .

After the hour of midnight had struck, and the church bells had solemnly knelled the departure of the old year, they burst out into cheery peals to welcome in the new – peals in which every note of melancholy was swallowed up in full-hearted joy. It was a case of *'L'an est mort. Vive l'an!'* The sweet, mellow tones of Fordington St George bells vied with those of St Peter's. Then the Volunteer Band started playing in Cornhill, and kept it up until after one o'clock. The programme of course included 'Auld Lang Syne' and 'God Save the Queen' [Victoria died, in fact, three weeks' later]. There was singing and cheering among the populace, encouraged by occasional supplication to 'liquid comfort'. Sundry libations were poured to Bacchus in the neighbourhood of the Town Pump, which seemed to be taken for an altar or pillar erected to that bibulous deity. At last, slowly but truly, came blessed silence, followed by sleep and oblivion. And thus the New Year had been ushered in.

Zitten Out The Wold Year

William Barnes

Men differ, as the journalist observed, in the attitude they assume at such times. For the pious, sociable clergyman William Barnes, New Year's Eve was a time to reaffirm friendships and family ties.

Why, rain or sheen, or blow or snow,
I zaid, if I could stand so's,
I'd come, vor all a friend or foe,
To sheake ye by the hand, so's;
An' spend, wi' kinsvo'k near an' dear,
A happy evenen, woonce a year,
A-zot wi' me'th
Avore the he'th
To zee the new year in, so's.
There's Jim an' Tom, a-grown the size
O' men, girt lusty chaps, so's,

An' Fanny wi' her sloo-black eyes,
Her mother's very daps, so's;
An' little Bill, so brown's a nut,
An' Poll, a gigglen little slut,
I hope will shoot
Another voot
The year that's comen in, so's.

An' there, upon his mother's knee,
So peart do look about, so's,
The little woone ov all, to zee
His vu'st wold year goo out, so's.
An' zoo mid God bless all o's still,
Gwain up or down along the hill,
To meet in glee
Agean to zee
A happy new year in, so's

The wold clock's han' do softly steal
Up roun' the year's last hour, so's;
Zoo let the han'-bells ring a peal,
Lik' them a-hung in tow'r, so's.
Here, here be two vor Tom, an' two
Vor Fanny, an' a peair vor you;
We'll meake em swing,
An' meake em ring,
The merry new year in so's.

Tom, mind your time there; you be wrong.
Come, let your bells all sound, so's:
A little clwoser, Poll; ding, dong!
There, now 'tis right all round, so's.
The clock's a-striken twelve, d'ye hear?
Ting, ting, ding, dong! Farewell, wold year!
'Tis gone, 'tis gone!—
Goo on, goo on,
An' ring the new woone in, so's!

Tenor's Out

Thomas Hardy

*The practice of muffling church bells on New Year's Eve, referred to by
the newspaper reporter, was witnessed by Hardy at St Peter's,
Dorchester, in 1884, and he preserved an account of it in his
autobiography.*

December 31st. To St Peter's belfry to the New-Year's-Eve ringing. The
night-wind whiffed in through the louvres as the men prepared the
mufflers with tar-twine and pieces of horse-cloth. Climbed over the bells to
fix the mufflers. I climbed with them and looked into the tenor bell: it is
worn into a bright pit where the clapper has struck so many years, and the
clapper is battered with its many blows.

The ringers now put their coats and waistcoats and hats upon the chimes
and clock and stand to. Old John is fragile, as if the bell would pull him up
rather than he pull the rope down, his neck being withered and white as his
white neckcloth. But his manner is severe as he says, 'Tenor out?' One of the
two tenor men gently eases the bell forward – that fine old E flat, my
father's admiration, unsurpassed in metal all the world over – and answers,
'Tenor's out'. Then old John tells them to 'Go!' and they start. Through long
practice he rings with the least possible movement of his body, though the
youngest ringers – strong, dark-haired men with ruddy faces – soon perspire
with their exertions. The red, green and white sallies bolt up through the
holes like rats between the huge beams overhead.

The Muffled Peal

Horace Moule

*Of the Dorset acquaintances of Hardy's youth, the closest male friendship
he ever formed was with Horace Moule, fourth of seven sons of the vicar
of Fordington (the parish between Stinsford and Dorchester), and brother
of Henry, the museum curator who recounted the legend of the lost pyx.
Horace Moule had a brilliant mind and an engaging personality, and was
destined for a successful academic career. There is a good deal of him in
Hardy's character Stephen Knight, the hero's rival in love in* A Pair of Blue
Eyes. *But Moule had a problem with alcohol, and perhaps opium, and
suffered bouts of depression. In 1873 he committed suicide.
During Hardy's adolescence in the 1850s, when he was articled to a
Dorchester architect, Moule inspired him to read widely in literature,
philosophy and the classics; and the following poem dates from this
period of relative stability in both their lives. Moule's poem was published
twenty years later, after his death, and was prefaced by a note explaining
that it was 'suggested by a midnight walk to Grey's Bridge, on the mild
and beautiful Old Year's Night of 1858'. Grey's Bridge, it will be recalled,
was where Hardy in* The Mayor of Casterbridge *made Henchard
meditate, and close to the Ten Hatches where he contemplated suicide.*

Flow gently, sweet Frome, under Grey's gleaming arches,
Where shines the white moon on thy cold sparkling wave;
Flow gently tonight, while Time silently marches
Fast hastening to lay the Old Year in his grave.

How tranquil the night is! the few sounds that break it
But draw deeper silence on meadow and hill:
Dogs barking, doors shutting, are all that awake it,
Or a hoof's distant clatter, now softer, now still.

The sands are fast ebbing; the Young Year undaunted,
Stands ready to run as his sire ran before;—

Grey's Bridge over the River Frome, which carries the main road into Dorchester from the east.

And shall no bell be rung, or no requiem chanted,
For the Old pilgrim dying before his son's door?

I said it half musing, when bells that, sweet sounding,
Seemed now like a distant chime, now like a dirge,
Sadly and strange through the calm air resounding,
Pealed from the turrets of knightly Saint George.

All muffled and mournful the tones they were ringing,
Now booming from far and now whispering near,
Wild voices of ghosts that were muttering, singing,
Wailing around an invisible bier.

But hark, they are still! the last echoes are sweeping
Down the lone valley where Frome's waters run;
The slow lingering hours, half smiling, half weeping,
Have left the dead Father to welcome the Son.

Now sounds the knell on the Tenor sonorous;
The last hour is come and the last breath is drawn;—
One moment more, and the whole pealing chorus
Seem changing the midnight to clamorous dawn!

So mournful before, now so joyous and cheerful,
Twofold is the story they sang to the stars:
I caught the twin echoes, the gay and the tearful,
And long will their music ring sweet in my ears.

Farewell, farewell, to the joy and the laughter
We've known in the years we are leaving behind!
Ah, who can tell us the friend that comes after
Will be like the old one, as pleasant, as kind?

Words, kisses, and smiles, in the year that is over
Drift far, far behind us while we hurry on;
Some poor paltry remnant may Memory recover,
The root glides away with the days that are gone.

'But say, did no sorrow embitter the pleasure?
Was gay laughter clouded with never a tear?
Are no wants, disasters, cares, griefs without measure,
Borne far away with the old parting year?

'Oh yes! and while Hopes, pointing upward, remind us
The new will be old, as the old was once new,
Let not the Past with sad memories blind us—
"Welcome" be said, while we murmur "Adieu".

'Then go forward boldly, and fearless of danger,
With souls that gain vigour from – graves of old years,

With hearts firm and ready to meet the young Stranger,
To smile with his laughter and weep with his tears!'

The river flows on down the lone valley wending,
The white moon is setting, the bells they are done;
Be joy to the New Year, kind blessings attending,
And peace evermore be with those that are gone.

New Year's Eve

Thomas Hardy

*Hardy himself could conceive the passing of the year on a cosmic scale,
and in a memorably sacrilegious poem, published in January 1907 (and
perhaps unthinkable a few years earlier) he had the temerity to hold a
conversation with God.*

'I have finished another year,' said God,
'In grey, green, white, and brown;
I have strewn the leaf upon the sod,
Sealed up the worm within the clod,
And let the last sun down.'

'And what's the good of it?' I said,
'What reasons made you call
From formless void this earth we tread,
When nine-and-ninety can be read
Why nought should be at all?

'Yea, Sire; why shaped you us, "who in
This tabernacle groan"—
If ever a joy be found herein,
Such joy no man had wished to win
If he had never known!'

Then he: 'My labours – logicless—
You may explain; not I:
Sense-sealed I have wrought, without a guess
That I evolved a Consciousness
To ask for reasons why.

'Strange that ephemeral creatures who
By my own ordering are,
Should see the shortness of my view,
Use ethic tests I never knew,
Or made provision for!'

He sank to raptness as of yore,
And opening New Year's Day
Wove it by rote as theretofore,
And went on working evermore
In his unweeting way.

Far From the Christmas Spirit

Nellie Titterington was in service as parlour-maid in the Hardy household during the 1920s, and forty years later she was persuaded to record some of her memories of life at Max Gate. Far from placing him on a par with the Almighty, the maids did not see Mr Hardy as a great literary figure, she recalled, but just another man, with no obviously impressive qualities. Christmas was a quiet day without any fuss, and birthdays were not noticeably different from other days. The usual daily routine was followed.

Hardy's two marriages were childless, so that in adult life he rarely, if ever, enjoyed the excitement of a Christmas spent among supercharged

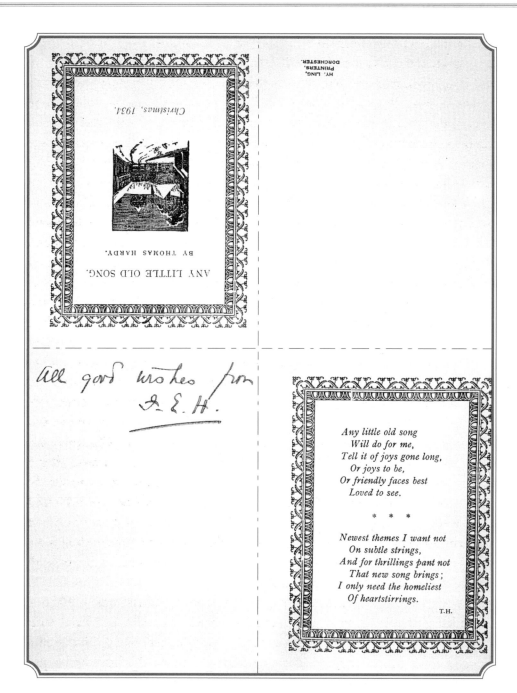

Christmas, 1934.

ANY LITTLE OLD SONG.

BY THOMAS HARDY.

HY. LING,
PRINTERS,
DORCHESTER.

*All good wishes from
F. E. H.*

Any little old song
Will do for me,
Tell it of joys gone long,
Or joys to be,
Or friendly faces best
Loved to see.

*   *   *

Newest themes I want not
On subtle strings,
And for thrillings pant not
That new song brings;
I only need the homeliest
Of heartstirrings.

T.H.

Christmas card (which would have been folded in four), sent in 1931 by Florence Hardy, the poet's widow, incorporating one of his poems. Florence, so much younger than him, survived her husband by less than a decade, dying in 1937.

children. This may help to account for the attitude he revealed in his correspondence. Writing about Christmas 1896, he told a friend: 'As you will imagine, our Christmas and new year here have been quite uneventful, except by post. But I agree with what Mrs Sheridan was saying to me a day or two ago, that a Christmas which brings no tragedies is upon the whole a thing to be thankful for when you have passed the time of life for expecting positive joys.' Two days earlier he had written: 'I have been all right in health and have had a Christmas of the dull kind which contents so-called "pessimists" like me – in its freedom from positive sorrows.' The gloom continued. To a correspondent at Christmas 1905 he sent a card which said simply: 'My dear Shorter: Many thanks. The same good wishes for you and Mrs Shorter. We are having a nice dull time here. Truly yours, T.H.' And on Boxing Day 1924 the sentiment was much the same: 'We have been as cheerful as may be this Christmas, and I hope you have also. But I long ago entered the region in a lifetime in which anniversaries are the saddest days of the year.'

Two Christmases were particularly dismal. Florence Dugdale, who was to become Hardy's second wife, was initiated into the Max Gate Christmas in 1910, and recalled the experience ruefully in a letter fifteen years later. 'My mind goes back to a Christmas day – 1910 – when I sat here alone, and vowed that no power on earth would ever induce me to spend another Christmas day at Max Gate. T.H. had gone off to Bockhampton to see his sisters, after a violent quarrel with the first Mrs T.H. because he wanted me to go to see the sisters too, and she said I shouldn't because they would poison my mind against her – and then – oh dear oh dear, what a scene – and he went off and she went up to her attic-study to write her memoirs until he came back at 8.30. It was the first Christmas of the kind I had ever spent, having always been with a party of cheerful people before that.'

But worse was to come. Hardy's penultimate Christmas – 1926 – coincided with the demise of Wessex, Florence's dog, who had lived with them all their married life together, and who was peculiarly affectionate towards them (and violently hostile to everyone else). 'We have had a sad aftering to our Christmas,' wrote Hardy to friends. 'Our devoted (and masterful) dog Wessex died on the 27th, and last night had his bed outside the house under the trees for the first time for thirteen years.' Florence was equally devastated: 'Of course he was merely a dog, and not a good dog always,' she wrote, 'but thousands (actually thousands) of afternoons and evenings I would have been alone but for him, and had always him to speak to. But I mustn't write about him, and I hope no one will ask me about him or mention his name.'

Max Gate in winter, recalled Nellie Titterington, was a grim, cold house. Once when she stoked up a welcoming fire for the return of Florence and distinguished guests (Siegfried Sassoon, T.E. Lawrence, and E.M. Forster), Hardy – with the excessive thrift which was an impoverished childhood's legacy – carefully removed with tongs all the lumps of coal which were not actually alight. One Christmas his gifts to the staff – a half-crown each left in small envelopes – were rejected as an insult, until Florence quadrupled them.

We stand indebted to the parlour-maid for her insights into the sombre, cheerless world of Christmas with Mr Hardy. On a lighter (or perhaps a heavier) note she has also favoured us, in her reminiscences, with the Max Gate cook's seasonal recipes:

MAX GATE, DORCHESTER. XMAS, 1926.

WITH THE THOUGHTS OF T.H. & F.E.H

The Hardys' Christmas card for 1926, showing their dog Wessex. No postman would have gone near him in his younger days, and the pathos of the card is that Wessex, by then aged thirteen, became painfully and terminally ill in December 1926, and was put down two days after Christmas.

Christmas Pudding

2 lb. raisins, 2 lb. currants, 1 lb. sultanas, 1½ lb. breadcrumbs, ½ lb. flour, 2 lbs. suet, ¼ lb. blanched almonds cut fine, 1 nutmeg, 1 teaspoonful mixed spice, 1 teaspoonful salt, rind of 2 lemons, chopped fine, 1 lb. moist sugar, 1 lb. mixed peel, 12 eggs, 1 teacupful milk, 1 wineglass rum, 1 wineglassful brandy, ½ pint stout or ale, juice of 2 lemons.

First mix all the dry ingredients well, beat the eggs; then make a hole in the middle of the dry mixture and pour this in. Thoroughly mix all together, boil for 7 hours in well buttered basins. This quantity will make three good puddings.

Sloe Gin

4 gallons best unsweetened gin, 4½ lb. best crystallised sugar, 6 quarts slit sloes, 2 quarts crushed sloes and kernels.

Mix these ingredients together. Place in cask in a room that is warm but has no fire. Roll and turn cask two or three times for several months; draw off after twelve months. Empty out sloes and return gin to cask for a month, then draw off, clear, and bottle.

Christmas Cake

6 oz. butter, 6 oz. raw sugar, 2 oz. treacle, 3 eggs, ¼ pint warm new milk, 1 lb. currants, ¼ lb. candied peel chopped, 1 oz. sweet almonds, 1 oz. bitter almonds chopped, ½ lb. flour.

Beat the butter to a cream, add the sugar and treacle and beat well. Then add the eggs whole, one by one, beating the mixture thoroughly between each. Add the milk very gradually, beat well a few minutes longer. Then add the currants, peel and almonds. Stir these in well, and lastly and very lightly add the flour. (If the flour is beaten with the other ingredients the cake will not be light) Bake in a moderate to slow oven for 3 hours.

As a tailpiece to this appetising interlude, it should be pointed out that the Christmas pudding may claim a peculiar literary distinction. It was referred to (in somewhat disparaging terms) in Hardy's last composition, his pencilled letter of Christmas Day, 1927. 'I am in bed on my back,' he wrote, 'living on butter-broth and beef tea, the servants being much concerned at my not being able to eat any Christmas pudding, though I am rather relieved . . .'

GREETINGS - - - from
Mr. and Mrs. THOMAS HARDY

Max Gate,
Dorchester.

Xmas, 1923

*Wessex, the Hardys' dog, outside Max Gate. The 1923 Christmas card, now in Dorset
County Museum.*

The Dead Quire

Thomas Hardy

*And so it is time to leave the old man, brooding in there on who knows
how many past Christmas nights (to borrow the description by Llewelyn
Powys with which this selection began). Hardy himself expressed his
pensive mood more poetically: 'The sad man sighed his phantasies: He
seems to sigh them still'.*

Beside the Mead of Memories,
Where Church-way mounts to Moaning Hill,
The sad man sighed his phantasies:
He seems to sigh them still.

''Twas the Birth-tide Eve, and the hamleteers
Made merry with ancient Mellstock zest,
But the Mellstock quire of former years
Had entered into rest.

'Old Dewy lay by the gaunt yew tree,
And Reuben and Michael a pace behind,
And Bowman with his family
By the wall that the ivies bind.

'The singers had followed one by one,
Treble, and tenor, and thorough-bass;
And the worm that wasteth had begun
To mine their mouldering place.

'For two-score years, ere Christ-day light,
Mellstock had throbbed to strains from these;
But now there echoed on the night
No Christmas harmonies.

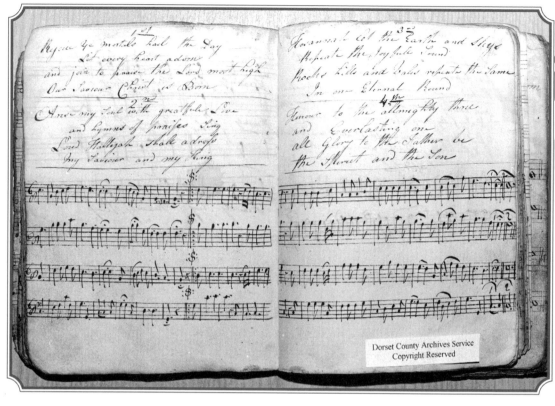

A manuscript carol book which belonged to a Puddletown musician, Stephen Arnold, in 1814.

'Three meadows off, at a dormered inn,
The youth had gathered in high carouse,
And, ranged on settles, some therein
Had drunk them to a drowse.

'Loud, lively, reckless, some had grown,
Each dandling on his jigging knee
Eliza, Dolly, Nance, or Joan—
Livers in levity.

'The taper flames and hearthfire shine
Grew smoke-hazed to a lurid light,
And songs on subjects not divine
Were warbled forth that night.

'Yet many were sons and grandsons here
Of those who, on such eves gone by,
At that still hour had throated clear
Their anthems to the sky.

'The clock belled midnight; and ere long
One shouted, "Now 'tis Christmas morn;
Here's to our women old and young,
And to John Barleycorn!"

'They drink the toast and shout again:
The pewter-ware rings back the boom,
And for a breath-while follows then
A silence in the room.

'When nigh without, as in old days,
The ancient quire of voice and string
Seemed singing words of prayer and praise
As they had used to sing:

'While shepherds watch'd their flocks by night,—
Thus swells the long familiar sound
In many a quaint symphonic flight—
To, Glory shone around.

'The sons defined their fathers' tones,
The widow his whom she had wed,
And others in the minor moans
The viols of the dead.

'Something supernal has the sound
As verse by verse the strain proceeds,
And stilly starring on the ground
Each roysterer holds and heeds.

'Towards its chorded closing bar
Plaintively, thinly, waned the hymn,

Yet lingered, like the notes afar
Of banded seraphim.

'With brows abashed, and reverent tread,
The hearkeners sought the tavern door:
But nothing, save wan moonlight, spread
The empty highway o'er.

'While on their hearing fixed and tense
The aerial music seemed to sink,
As it were gently moving thence
Along the river brink.

'Then did the Quick pursue the Dead
By crystal Froom that crinkles there;
And still the viewless quire ahead
Voiced the old holy air.

'By Bank-walk wicket, brightly bleached,
It passed, and 'twixt the hedges twain,
Dogged by the living; till it reached
The bottom of Church Lane.

'There, at the turning, it was heard
Drawing to where the churchyard lay:
But when they followed thitherward
It smalled, and died away.

'Each headstone of the quire, each mound,
Confronted them beneath the moon;
But no more floated therearound
That ancient Birth-night tune.

'There Dewy lay by the gaunt yew tree,
There Reuben and Michael, a pace behind,
And Bowman with his family
By the wall that the ivies bind . . .

'As from a dream each sobered son
Awoke, and musing reached his door:
'Twas said that of them all, not one
Sat in a tavern more.'

—The sad man ceased; and ceased to heed
His listener, and crossed the leaze
From Moaning Hill towards the mead—
The Mead of Memories.

*The Mead of Memories. Graves to children who died about the time of Hardy's own death, in
the extension to Stinsford graveyard, between the church and the river.*

ACKNOWLEDGEMENTS

Anyone researching Hardy will find a rich store of material and expert help within a few minutes' walk of his statue at the Top o' Town, Dorchester. My foremost debt of gratitude is to Shirley Wickham, Local Studies Librarian, and her colleagues in Dorchester Reference Library. Equally helpful, in tracing illustrations and stray references, has been Lilian Swindall at Dorset County Museum. My friends in the Dorset Record Office have, as always, made me welcome, and assisted in every possible way.

I should also like to thank: the staff of Wiltshire and Bath library services, and the Wiltshire and Swindon Record Office; Roger Trim and Nick Thomas for allowing me to photograph them; Mr T.W. Jesty, churchwarden of Stinsford; Derek Parker for photographic processing; Lisa Hyland of Macmillan; and Jaqueline Mitchell and Alison Flowers of Sutton Publishing. I am indebted, too, to my wife Alison, and other friends who have witnessed me becoming a Hardy fanatic as my research has progressed.

Desmond Hawkins kindly agreed to read my work in typescript, and made several helpful suggestions. For this kindness, and for his general encouragement over many years, I have taken the liberty of dedicating the book to him. For its shortcomings I am alone responsible.

Sources

Quotations from the works of Thomas Hardy are included (except where indicated below) by kind permission of Macmillan General Books. Poems by William Barnes are from the Centaur Press edition by Bernard Jones (1962). I should like to express my gratitude to the copyright owners (named below) of works by other writers for permission to quote from their material. In the few instances where I have failed to track down owners of work still in copyright, I offer an apology, and a hope that, should they see this book, they would approve of its contents.

The following list gives bibliographical references for extracts in their order of appearance in the book. The novels, poems, autobiography, and letters of Thomas Hardy, the poems of William Barnes, and letters of Florence Hardy (for which see Martin Millgate (ed.), *Letters of Emma and Florence Hardy*, 1996) are excluded.

Llewelyn Powys, *Skin for Skin*, 1925, pp.119–20 (by kind permission of the estate of Llewelyn Powys, and Jonathan Cape)

H.G. Mundy, *The Journal of Mary Frampton*, 2nd edn, 1885, pp. 365–6

Diaries of Alice and Emily Smith: DRO D500/4,6 (by kind permission of Dorset Record Office and Mrs M.B. Costabadie)

Louisa Colfox's Toast : DRO D/COL/F23 (by kind permission of Dorset Record Office and Sir John Colfox)

Thomas Hardy, 'The Thieves who Couldn't Stop Sneezing', in Pamela Dalziel (ed.), *Thomas Hardy: the excluded and collaborative stories*, 1992, pp. 52–65 (by kind permission of the trustees of the Hardy Estate)

John Symonds Udal, 'Christmas in Dorsetshire', *Notes and Queries*, 6th series, vol. 2, 1880, p. 504

John Symonds Udal, *Dorsetshire Folklore*, 1922

William Holloway, *Scenes of Youth*, 1803

William Archer, 'Real conversations: conversation 1: with Mr Thomas Hardy', *The Critic* (New York), 1901 (reprinted 1979)

The Battle of Waterloo: typescript copies in Dorset County Museum and Dorchester Reference Library (by kind permission of the English Folk Dance and Song Society)

Hardy Players: *Dorset County Chronicle*, 30.12.1920, p. 2, col. 4

Gertrude Bugler, 'Christmas Night at Max Gate, 1920', *Thomas Hardy Society Review*, 1982, pp. 235–7 (by kind permission of Christine S. O'Connor)

M.E. Francis, 'Mrs Sibley and the Sexton', *Dorset Dear*, 1905, pp. 207–21

William Plomer (ed.), *The Diaries of Francis Kilvert*, vol.3, 1940, p. 354

Henry Moule, 'Cross Hand Stone', *Somerset and Dorset Notes and Queries*, vol. 1, 1889, p. 247

The Mellstock Club: *Dorset County Chronicle*, 11.2.1919, p. 4, col. 3

Pope, Alfred, 'Some dew ponds in Dorset', *Proceedings of the Dorset Natural History and Antiquarian Society*, vol. 33, 1912, pp. 22–33

Ralph Wightman, *Moss Green Days*, 1947 (by kind permission of Laurence Pollinger Ltd and the estate of Ralph Wightman)

W.H. Hudson, *Nature in Downland*, 1900, pp. 248–53

A Fine Moonlight Evening: *Dorset County Chronicle*, 3.1.1901, p. 4, cols. 4–5

Horace Moule, 'The Muffled Peal', in Handley C.G. Moule, *Dorchester Poems*, 1878, pp. 24–6

Titterington, Ellen, 'The Domestic Life of Thomas Hardy (1921–1928)', *Thomas Hardy Monographs*, no. 4, 1963

Recipes: Ellen Titterington, 'Afterthoughts of Max Gate', *Thomas Hardy Monographs*, no. 59, 1969

Picture Credits

The compiler and publisher would like to acknowledge the following for permission to use illustrations (the copyright owners of the illustrations on pages 3, 102 and 106 have not been traced):

Dorset Natural History and Archaeological Society (Dorset County Museum), pages, ii, 8, 41, 56, 84, 87, 89, 90, 92, 95, 99, 124, 140, 142, 144

Dorset County Council Archives Service (Dorset Record Office), pages 6 (T/STF), 88 (PE/PUD:AO1/1/2), 146 (D/WPC/Z5)]

Dorset County Council Library Service (Dorchester Reference Library), pages 3, 71, 81

Executors of Clare Leighton (by kind permission of David R. Leighton), pages 9, 14, 25, 118

The Donald Maxwell Estate, page 2

The following photographs were taken by the compiler during 1997: pages 16, 37, 77, 85, 100, 112, 136, 149

The picture on page 152 is by William Strang (1859–1921), and was drawn in 1916 when Thomas Hardy was seventy-six.